COLLINS

Design and Technology
Textiles
Foundation Course

Eileen Chapman
Associate Deputy Head (Curriculum)
William Farr CofE Comprehensive School, Welton

Janet Inglis
Head of Design and Technology
Hanson School, Bradford

Sue Plews
Head of Technology Faculty,
Walton School for Girls

CollinsEducational
An imprint of HarperCollins*Publishers*

CONTENTS

Published by Collins Educational
An imprint of HarperCollins*Publishers* Ltd
77–85 Fulham Palace Road
London W6 8JB
The HarperCollins website address is www.**fire**and**water**.com

First published 1999

ISBN 000 329492 7

British Library Cataloguing in Publication Data
A catalogue record for this book is available from the British Library.

Designed by Ken Vail Graphic Design
Cover Design by Ken Vail Graphic Design
Cover photograph: Angus Mill, Gerber Ltd
Illustrated by: Simon Girling & Associates (Mike Lacey), Nick Hawken,
Linda Rogers Associates (Lorna Barnard), Ross Thomson, Ken Vail Graphic Design
Printed and bound by Scotprint
Commissioned by: Alison Walters
Edited by: Tamsin Miller
Production: Anna Pauletti

WHAT IS TEXTILES TECHNOLOGY?

Design and Technology (D&T) is an exciting subject where you can design and make products in different materials. This book looks at how to design and make textile products.

Through D&T you will use your knowledge of subjects such as maths, science and art to help you to design products. Information technology (IT) skills are also very important. You will be encouraged to use all of these skills.

As you progress through school you will probably be offered the chance to take one of the options in D&T at examination level. The diagram on the right shows how you can follow your chosen option through school to higher education if you wish. Alternatively you may decide to go straight from school to work.

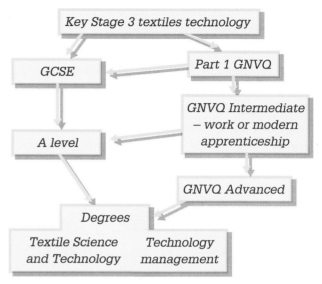

Key Stage 3 textiles technology

GCSE

Part 1 GNVQ

GNVQ Intermediate – work or modern apprenticeship

A level

GNVQ Advanced

Degrees
Textile Science and Technology   Technology management

Textiles technology can lead to many exciting and well-paid opportunities. The following are some of the possible careers in the textiles industry:

- Fashion designer – designs mass produced items or one off garments;
- Designer of other textile products – designs products which use fabric;
- Pattern designer – designs fabrics;
- Colourist – makes sure that fabrics are dyed correctly;
- Quality Controller – responsible for the final quality of all products made in a factory. This includes planning which tests will be carried out and how they will be tested;
- Production manager – responsible for the smooth running of the factory;
- Production director – makes sure that sufficient raw materials and equipment are available to produce the product at the right quality. Also responsible for motivating the work force;
- Buyer – sources fabrics or garments from all over the world.

Colourists at work

Paris and Milan are important centres for fashion

To be aware of new trends designers need to travel to fashion fairs and markets around the world.

The textile industry is important in Britain, more than 370,000 people work in about 12,000 companies throughout the country. Many of our textile products are exported. This creates wealth for the country to ensure that we enjoy a high standard of living.

Whatever career you follow when you leave school, textiles technology will help you to develop skills in planning, prioritising, communication and working as part of a team. Many employers look for people with a high level of skill in these areas.

Dior in Paris

Italian designers Dolce & Gabbana

1 DESIGNING

The process of designing and making a product can be divided into groups of activities.
The diagram shown in Fig. 1.1 shows the design process and the stages involved in it. In order to make it easier to understand, the process is shown as a line, but it is in fact more like the circular process shown in Fig. 1.2. For example, once you have made something and evaluated it (noted its good or bad points), you could go through the whole process again and improve your design. Alternatively you may begin designing by evaluating something which has already been made by you or someone else.

1 Starting points
Contexts
Identifying needs
Design briefs
Evaluating existing products

2 Generating a design proposal
Drawing up a specification
Sketching and modelling
Ideas
Evaluating ideas
Choosing ideas

3 Planning and making
Product planning
Resource planning
Action planning
Making

4 Evaluating
Final evaluation
Other people's evaluation
Improving your finished product

Fig. 1.1
A linear design process

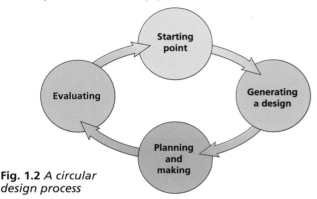

Fig. 1.2 *A circular design process*

Design frameworks

Designing might seem to be a complicated activity with many different things to think about. But, designing products is not difficult if you know what to do. If you were sent on an errand to a place that you had not been to before you would probably be given a map marked with a route. In Design and Technology (D&T) you can use a series of design frameworks as a route through the design process.
These frameworks will help you to design and make quality products.

Design frameworks will guide you through the development of your product. When you begin designing and making they may give you a lot of help. As you develop your designing skills you will do more of the work yourself. Gradually you will take control of your work and the design framework will be made up of a series of headings for each part of the project. Fig. 1.3 shows one example of frameworks. You can see that a lot of the work has already been done for you.

Context	Brief	
Teenagers bedrooms have many small items to store. Without adequate storage the bedroom begins to look untidy. Make a list of the small items you need to store in your bedroom like CD's or pencils.	A brief is a statement which tells other people what you are going to do. Complete the following brief: I am going to design and make... **Analysis** Finding out more about what you have to do is known as analysing the situation. Answer the following questions in full sentences. 1 How much time will you have to make and evaluate your design?	2 What do I want my finished item to store? 3 List the different shapes you could use. 4 List the different fabrics you could use. 5 How much will it cost to make? 6 Do I want my finished article to hang up? 7 Do I need to use any special colours? 8 Is there anything else I need to know in order to finish this work?
Name	**Form**	**D&T Teacher**

Fig. 1.3 *A design framework*

Starting points

There are several ways of starting to design textile products. These starting points will change as your designing skills develop.

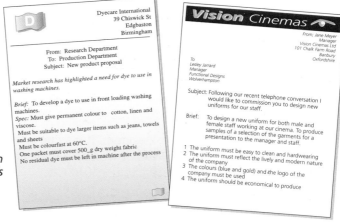

Fig. 1.4 *Design briefs*

Design briefs

You may be given a brief which will tell you what you have to design and make. You will need to think carefully about the brief and try to work out exactly what is required. Professional designers are often given a brief by their customer or client. The final function of the product is identified, but its final design features, the colour and choice of fabric may be left for the designer to decide.

Fig. 1.5 *Working from a context*

◀ Contexts

You may be given a context or situation to work from. Often the context is a particular problem that you are asked to solve. You will be expected to investigate the context, work out what is required and write your own design brief to solve the problem. For example, 'I am going to design and make an item which will help me to keep my bedroom tidy.

Identifying needs

Working from a context often involves looking at other peoples needs and requirements. Everyone has basic needs - as human beings we need air, water, food, shelter and warmth for our survival. In addition to these we have other 'wants' depending on our situation. In the Stone Age, people kept themselves warm by wearing animal skins but today we want our clothing to say something about us. Clothing today can be used as a fashion statement or to show that we belong to a particular group.

In some situations clothing is used to protect people as they carry out their jobs or hobbies. These clothes need particular properties, without these properties the clothing would not be functional.

Fig. 1.6 *Clothing can show that we belong to a particular group*

Fig. 1.7 *Some clothing needs special properties*

Evaluating existing products ➡

Working from existing products is another way to start designing. You may be asked to improve an existing product or to re-design it completely. By evaluating existing products you can study how other designers have used the materials and technology available to them.

You should begin evaluating a product by looking at it carefully, try to work out the original aims of the designer. It may be possible for you to test the product to find out how well it works. Use the checklist in Fig. 1.8 to help you.

Once you understand a product and its function you can begin to suggest improvements. Sometimes minor alterations can make a product more functional or more attractive.

Checklist

1 What were the designer's original aims? Draw up what you think was there design specification

2 How well does the product meet the specification?

3 How well does the product work?

4 How well is the product made?

5 What fabrics and notions have been used for the product? Are they suitable?

6 Is the product environmentally friendly?

7 What improvements to the product can you suggest?

Fig. 1.8 *Design checklist*

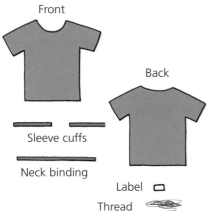

Front

Back

Sleeve cuffs

Neck binding

Label ▭

Thread

Fig. 1.9 *Disassembled product*

⬅ Disassembly

Disassembly means taking a product to pieces. This is an excellent way to find out how a product was made. It is possible to take a product to pieces and use the pieces to make a new pattern. However, do not take anything apart without permission or without being told to do so! It is possible to imagine what the parts of a product would look like without actually taking the product apart. Begin by making sketches of the product. Try to draw the pattern pieces that were used to make it. Look at the insides of the product. How is it stitched together? What types of seams have been used? Examine the fastenings, pockets and decorative stitching. Enlarge these features in your drawings to show the detail.

Once this detailed examination of the product is complete you may want to ask yourself some questions about it.

What method of construction was used for the fabric?

What fibres or fabrics were used?

What type of fastening has been used? Could any other fastening be used instead?

Do the fabrics used have any special properties which are needed by the product?

What trimmings have been used? Do these improve the product?

What colour has been chosen? How important is the colour?

How well do you think that the product meets the original aims of the designer?

How has the fabric been decorated? Is this decoration important to the finished product?

Is the product suitable for the function for which it was designed?

Fig. 1.10 *Examining the product*

Generating design proposals
Investigating

In D&T, looking very carefully at something or studying it in detail is called investigation. This means finding out as much as you can about a situation or product. You will need to investigate the design brief or the context in order to find out what you need to do.

Fig. 1.11 *There are many sources of information*

Investigating will involve many different skills and sources of information. Try to use as wide a variety of sources as you can. A lot of useful information can be accessed by computer – databases, CD ROM's and the Internet, are excellent resources for your investigations. Books, magazines and catalogues can also give you information about situations or products, or you may be able to find useful material from films or TV. It is also a good idea to talk to people who would use, manufacture or sell the products which you will design.

Talking to people or making observations yourself is known as **primary** information. Using books or information gathered by other people is called **secondary** information. You should use both primary and secondary sources of information in your investigations.

Brainstorming

When you start to design you need to create as many different ideas as you can – even ones which sound unlikely should be included. Brainstorming is a good way of recording all of your first ideas, whether you are working alone or in a group. When you are organising a brainstorming session it may be useful to follow the simple rules shown in Fig. 1.12.

Research boards ➡

Research boards (also sometimes called mood or theme boards) are often used by designers to help them think of ideas. Pictures of products which are similar to the product you are designing are mounted on a board. Once you have collected a variety of images and mounted them on your board you can add notes on the features of each product, the trimmings or types of fastenings used. You may want to add other notes such as the cost of individual items, or

Brainstorming rules

1 Choose someone to record the ideas that are suggested. They can be written on a flip chart, a chalkboard or a large sheet of paper.
2 Write down everything that the group can think of that is related to the topic. Remember that any idea is worth writing down at this stage.
3 Don't be tempted to discuss the ideas as you think of them. Write them down first and discuss them later.
4 Try to prevent the brainstorming session from going on too long. Set a time in which to work – 15 to 20 minutes should be long enough.

Fig. 1.12 *Brainstorming rules*

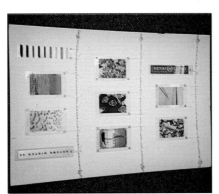

Fig. 1.14 *A research board*

highlight parts which you particularly like. These parts may then be incorporated into your own ideas. Further uses of research boards can be found on page 15.

Spider diagrams

Spider diagrams are a useful way of recording a brainstorming session. Begin by writing the topic in the centre of a blank piece of paper and then write each idea around it. You could draw a line to link each idea to the topic. Allow the diagram to grow as ideas are recorded.

Fig. 1.13 *A spider diagram*

Asking the experts

A good way to start your investigation is to contact people who are experts on the subject you are researching. This a useful form of **primary research**. Experts may include designers, manufacturers or retailers. People who use products are also a source of expert information. Imagine that you were researching costumes for a dance company. The dancers would be able to give you information about their needs which you may not have thought about.

Fig. 1.15 *Example of a fax cover*

Collecting information

Contacting experts will probably mean writing letters, telephoning or using e-mail. It is always a good idea to show any letters to your teacher before you post them. Find out if there is a fax machine in school which you can use. A fax combines the speed of a phone call with the advantages of a letter. Once you have contacted the relevant expert you may be able to arrange a visit.

Interviews

If you wish to interview someone you should arrange a convenient time and place to meet. You must introduce yourself and explain the reason for the interview. Be prepared, take a list of questions with you so you make the most of your time. It is useful to record answers on a tape recorder (if the person you are interviewing does not mind).

Questionnaires

Questionnaires are another useful way of collecting primary information. You may have access to a computer program which will help you to write the questionnaire and allow you to analyse the information you collect.

Before you begin to write your questionnaire, decide on the following points:

What do I want to find out? – only ask questions about this.

Who will I ask? – remember to only ask people who would buy or use the product.

The best way to record your answers – is it better to use a tape recorder or a tally chart or would individual questionnaires be the best way to collect information?

Questions which require one word answers such as a yes or no are called closed questions. For example, 'Should the item be machine washable?'

Questions which require more detail are known as open questions. For example, 'Explain why it would be better to use woven rather than knitted fabric for a sports bag.'

Multiple choice questions can also be used, these give the person answering a number of choices.

Internet

Using the Internet will allow you to make 'virtual visits' to a wide range of art galleries, museums and fashion designers. You can even contact other schools to share your ideas.

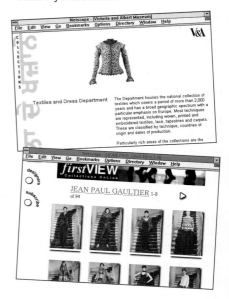

Fig. 1.16 *Websites on the internet*

Museums and exhibitions

Museums display a large amount of information which has been collected over the years. Seeing how designs have changed over the years can be interesting and useful for your design work. Some modern fashion designers include 'retro' work in their portfolios, these are designs based on previous, retrospective, fashion trends. 'Retro' work can be included in interior design, clothing and accessories. Museums are an excellent source of information if you are designing costumes or sets for theatre work.

Fig. 1.17 *Museums are a good source of information*

Design specifications

Constraints

When you are carrying out your investigations it is important to think about all the things that may affect your product. The time you have to work in, your own skills and the money available will all need to be considered before you draw up a specification for your product. These things are called constraints and they will have an important effect on your work. Often the constraints are written in the brief by the client.

cost
safety
materials available
time to make
making skills
washability
secure construction

Fig. 1.18 *Constraints on the design of a play mat for babies*

My playmat should:
- cost no more than £5.00 to make;
- be safe;
- be suitable for a baby of eight to twelve months to use;
- be possible to be made in six lessons;
- require some machine sewing;
- be washable.

Fig. 1.19 *Simple specification*

Criteria

Once you have identified the constraints affecting your design you can work out the criteria that your product needs to satisfy - that is, the things it has to do. You should make a list of the criteria that your product must meet. This forms your design specification. You may write a simple **specification** which lists the criteria in any order of importance. Alternatively you may write a more detailed specification which will divide the criteria into two groups, essential and desirable.

Essential criteria are the things your product **must** satisfy. **Desirable criteria** are the criteria your product **should** satisfy if possible.

It is important to develop a list of specific things your product must do. If you have a detailed specification you will find it easier to evaluate and develop your ideas. The number of decisions you will need to make will be limited as the specification will guide you.
The specification will provide a check list which you can use to test your ideas against. Specifications are also used to check the finished product to show that you have been successful in meeting your criteria.

Essential criteria:
My play mat must -
- be possible to make in six lessons;
- be suitable for a baby of eight to twelve months to use;
- be of educational value to the baby;
- measure between 400 cm and 500 cm square;
- cost no more than £5.00 to make;
- require some machine sewing;
- be safe;
- be washable.

Desirable criteria:
My play mat should -
- be decorated by hand;
- be suitable for mass production;
- use a range of colours.

Make a list of essential and desirable criteria for:

1. a teenager's bag;

2. a fabric shopping bag or baby's holdall.

Compare the lists and explain differences.

Fig. 1.20 *A more detailed specification*

Ideas

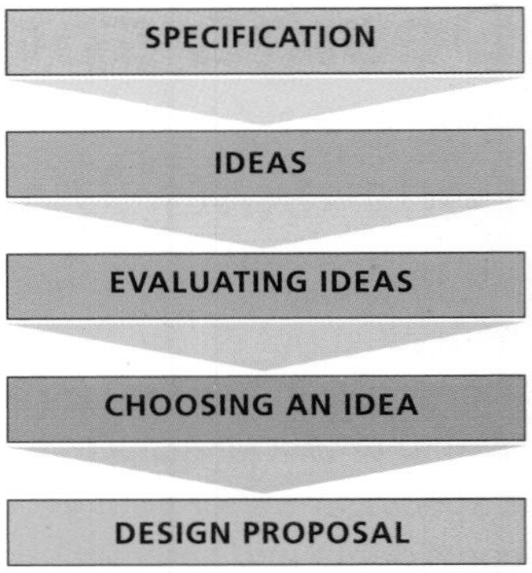

Once you have drawn up a specification the next stage in generating a design proposal is to start thinking about ideas. The aim is to begin with a number of ideas and develop one of them into a design proposal. Fig. 1.21 shows the stages in the design process.

SPECIFICATION

IDEAS

EVALUATING IDEAS

CHOOSING AN IDEA

DESIGN PROPOSAL

Fig. 1.21 *Stages in the design process*

First ideas – using your specification

Deciding what you could design and make can be the hardest part for some people. Don't worry if you do not feel inspired! The specification will help you because it provides you with a detailed list of criteria which your product should satisfy. At this stage try to produce as many ideas as you can. Try to be creative – ideas which you may think are very silly at first may be of use later. Look at the idea in Fig. 1.22 (there are some other examples on page 92). These are products which are being developed. Remember to compare your ideas with your specification as you work, checking that your ideas will satisfy the criteria you have decided are important.

Fig. 1.22 *Fabric of the future will allow us to send e-mail to our friends while walking down the street*

1. Investigate the development of swimwear over the years. Look at the changing fashion in relation to the changing role of women.

2. Look at these pictures in Fig. 1.23. Can you identify where the inspiration for the designs came from?

Sources of inspiration

Designers get their ideas from many different sources. One way to find ideas is to look at existing products. Ask yourself questions about the products. What do you like about them? What works in the design? What could be changed to improve the design?

Nature can be a good source of ideas both for surface decoration patterns and for three dimensional (3D) shapes for garments or accessories. Make a collection of leaves, shells, pictures of birds or animals. Draw some of these items. How could you use these to help your design?

Sometimes fashion ideas are developed based on needs. During World War II fabric was in short supply. Skirts became shorter, trousers narrower, jackets had only one or two buttons to fasten, epaulettes and large collars were not used. This made use of the small amount of fabric which was available. After the war, when fabric was more readily available skirts became fuller and longer, and trousers became wider.

Fig. 1.23

Fig. 1.24 *'New look' and utility clothes*

Recording ideas

Ideas are quickly forgotten if you do not record them. The quickest and easiest way to record your ideas is to draw them. If you are using a book for inspiration you may decide to photocopy the pictures, or use illustrations from magazines. Scanning images on to a computer or using a digital camera to take photographs are alternative ways of recording ideas.

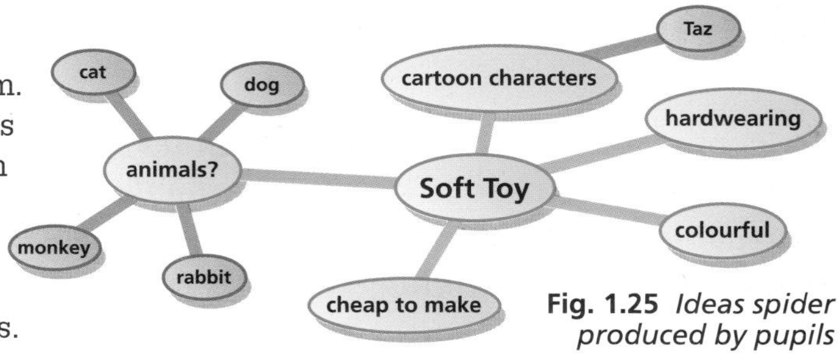

Fig. 1.25 *Ideas spider produced by pupils*

Modelling is another way of recording ideas, but this will take more time than drawing. For some items modelling will help you to communicate your ideas more clearly than drawing or writing (see page 25). Whatever method you choose, your work must be easy to understand and well presented so that other people are able to follow your ideas.

Freehand sketching ➡

Freehand sketching is a good way to record and present your ideas quickly. Ideas can be sketched in a variety of different media such as: pencils; ball pens and fine line pens. Sketch quickly and lightly. Your aim is to get your ideas down on paper as quickly as you can. (See page 16 for details of figure sketching.)

Fig. 1.26 *Ideas sketched by pupils*

Sketching in 3D

Some ideas in Fig. 1.26 have been drawn in two dimensions (2D) and others in 3D. 2D drawings show only two basic measurements (dimensions) – height and width. 3D drawings show three basic measurements – height, width and depth. 3D drawings show more information and make your ideas look more realistic.

It is sometimes helpful to draw a 3D box and then draw objects inside, using the box as a guide. This is known as **crating**. As you become more experienced you will find that you can draw in 3D without using crates.

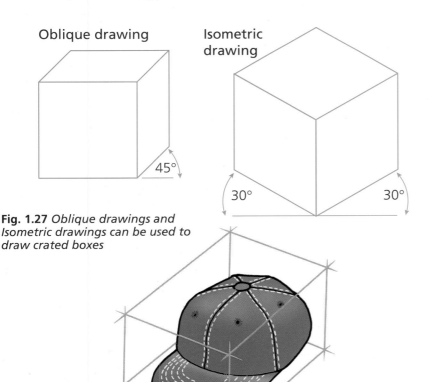

Oblique drawing

Isometric drawing

45°

30°   30°

Fig. 1.27 *Oblique drawings and Isometric drawings can be used to draw crated boxes*

Fig. 1.28 *Hat drawn inside a crate to give 3D effect*

Practise drawing 3D diagrams of textile products. You could include the following: bags; bed linen; hats.
Start by using crates to help you.

Using colour

Colour is important in our lives, it can be used to create different effects and moods. It is also used to communicate information about our surroundings. Companies often have a particular colour associated with their logo. These colours are chosen carefully to give a particular message. Choosing the colours for your design can be a difficult task. The right choice will make the design look more attractive – the wrong choice of colours gives the wrong image and can spoil an otherwise good piece of work.

The colour wheel ➡

Red, blue and yellow are known as **primary** colours. These colours cannot be made by mixing other colours together. By mixing the primary colours we create **secondary** colours.

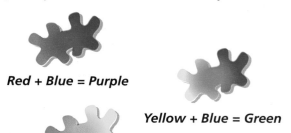

Red + Blue = Purple

Yellow + Blue = Green

Red + Yellow = Orange

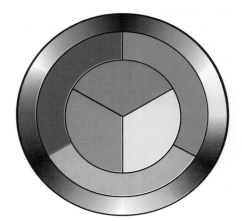

Fig. 1.29 *Colour wheel*

Tertiary colours are created by mixing a primary colour and a secondary colour.

By adding black or white to the colours we can create different **tones**.

Warm and cold colours ➡

Reds, oranges and yellows are said to be warm colours. Blues and greens are known as cold colours. Warm colours appear to be bigger and closer to you than cold colours. Objects which are coloured with cold colours look smaller and further away.

Fig. 1.30 *Which looks smaller? Which one seems to be furthest away?*

(a)

(b)

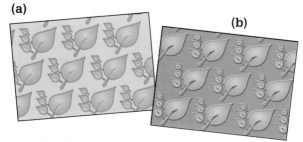

Fig. 1.31 *(a) harmonious colours and (b) contrasting colours*

⬅ Harmony and contrast

Colours which are close to each other on the colour wheel create harmony. Harmonious colours are used to create peaceful feelings. Colours which are opposite each other are said to be complimentary. These colours will create a contrast. Contrasting colours can create a startling effect.

Colour association

In all cultures colours have a particular significance. Particular colours may be associated with different activities or cultural festivals. In Britain brides often wear white wedding dresses, but in Asia they wear red. In China white is associated with death, but in Britain, black is the colour of mourning.

Different colours are often used to tell the sexes apart – *which is the baby boy?*

Fig. 1.32

Black is associated with the night and death, black can be the colour of uniforms and authority.

White is the colour of snow. It suggests purity and is used for christenings and weddings.

Red is associated with fire, danger, anger, love, the heart and evil. Red is a warm, vibrant colour.

Yellow reminds us of the sun. It is used by Buddhists to symbolise life and truth. It is a very stimulating colour and should be used in small quantities.

Blue is the colour of the sky and sea. It is used to show honesty, truth, peace and wisdom. Blue is a peaceful, calming colour.

Green is a calm colour, reminding us of the natural world. It represents safety, growth and hope. It can be used to represent 'environmentally friendly' products.

Orange is a bright, cheerful colour, used to represent power. It can be very intense and should be used sparingly.

Purple is a rich colour, associated with royalty. It is used to represent wealth and luxury.

1. Which colours would you use for the following?

   The fairy or witch in a pantomime.
   A valentines card.
   A birthday card for your elderly aunt.
   A birthday card for a young brother.
   A warning sign.

2. Collect samples of logos of different companies. What message is the company trying to pass to the consumer by their use of colour?

Research boards

Textile designers often develop their ideas by making a research board. This is a very good way of presenting research materials. The board should include a wide selection of reference material showing the colours, shapes and motifs which reflect the theme you are studying. Postcards, photographs, magazine cuttings, images from holiday brochures, colours from paint charts and pieces of fabrics are all useful as a starting point when developing your ideas.

Use a large sheet of paper or card, A3 or A2 would be ideal. Take different samples of colours and shapes. Stick these samples together to create the mood you need for your design. These should try to make your mood board look interesting. Use different

Fig. 1.33 *Research boards are used in industry*

shapes, these may represent the images you are working with. If you are trying to create a natural feel with greens and browns you could use leaf or tree shapes.

Research boards may be used to show new colour combinations, these are sometimes known as colour boards. Colour boards will show the way in which the colours work together, and should include fabric samples to show the way the colours will be used to create pattern and texture.

15

Fashion sketching

When designing clothing it is necessary to display the clothes on a figure. The pose of the figure should reflect the style of clothes, relaxed for casual clothing or a smarter pose for more formal clothes.

Every designer has their own style of drawing which can take many years to develop. Collect fashion drawings from magazines and compare drawing styles. To begin with it is useful to have a figure which you can use as the basis for your drawings.

A simple way to create a template which you can draw round is to scan images into the computer. These can be saved as templates which you could use to draw round in the future.

Figure proportions

To achieve a good figure the head is used as a measurement:

A balance line is usually drawn from the neck to the foot which is taking the weight of the body. Look at the sketches on the right, see how the balance line is used to give a good balance to the figure. Which figure would you use for casual clothing? Which for more formal clothing? Why?

Use tracing paper over your template, this will allow you to obtain the correct proportions for your fashion sketches. A **light box** will make this much easier. Develop the design lightly over the figure, using a pencil. Carefully add details such as seams, pockets, fastenings etc. You can then add more details, showing folds and shadows on the fabric. Children are harder to draw than adults as their proportions alter as they grow, young children have a large head in proportion to their bodies.

Collect photographs or illustrations of children at different ages. Work out the proportions of their head to their bodies.

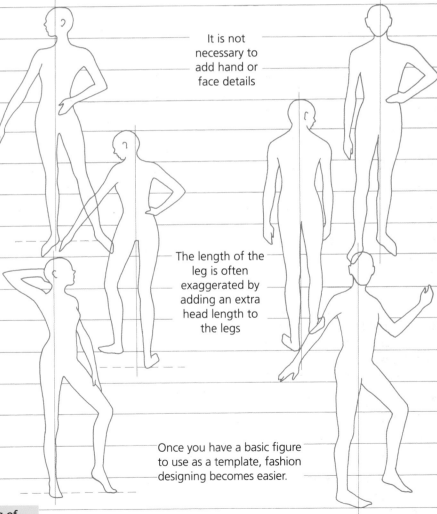

For women the head will fit into the body 7.5 times

For men the proportion is 7.5 or 8 'heads' are used for the body

It is not necessary to add hand or face details

The length of the leg is often exaggerated by adding an extra head length to the legs

Once you have a basic figure to use as a template, fashion designing becomes easier.

Fig. 1.34 *Templates for females*

Fig. 1.35 *Templates for males*

Graphic media

Graphic media describes anything which can be used to create a drawing, picture or painting. Pencils, markers, paints, cameras and computer software are all graphic media. To begin with all you need are pencils and paper.

There is a large selection of graphic materials available (see pages 11–12 *Collins Design and Technology Foundation Course*). It is important to take care of your materials – make sure that pencils are sharp and brushes and palettes are clean and ready for use.

Line Drawings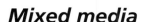

A variety of pens and pencils may be used for line drawing. Fine liners will give a very clear line and are excellent for accurate detailed work. Roller pens, ball points and fibre tipped pens can all be used, each giving a different effect. Experiment with a variety of pens to find which you prefer to work with. Pencils can also be used for line drawings or for adding shades.

Coloured pencils are available in a wide range of colours, and are easy to use. Pencils are useful for creating different tones, this is achieved by using more pressure. They are also good for mixing to create different colours.

Fig. 1.36 *Line drawings*

Fig. 1.37 *Drawing coloured in pencil crayons*

Mixed media

In fashion drawing it is normal to use a variety of media to achieve the final drawing. The sketch in Fig. 1.38 was produced in four stages.

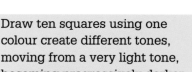

Draw ten squares using one colour create different tones, moving from a very light tone, becoming progressively darker.

1. The drawing was sketched in pencil.

2. Colour was added, as was shading in one direction, giving a darker tone on one side to give the effect of light.

3. Darker tone was added to the folds, a soft pencil was used to create the effect of texture and a fine liner used to add details.

4. White was added to give highlights and a more realistic effect, a thick black outline was added. The figure was then cut out and mounted on clean card.

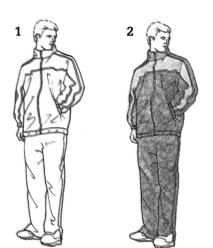
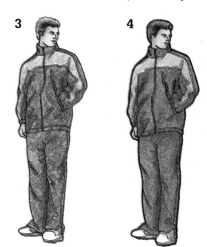

Fig. 1.38 *Development of drawing*

Working drawings

Once ideas have been developed, a working drawing needs to be produced. Working drawings show the product from each view, highlighting the positioning of any details such as pockets, fasteners, seams etc. These drawings are normally annotated. This means that notes are included to prevent any confusion or uncertainty. These drawings need to be detailed as they may be used by other people.

Any detail which cannot be shown clearly in the drawing should be shown separately, with notes which explain anything which cannot be shown by the drawing alone.

Pattern and texture

When developing fashion sketches or working drawings you may wish to add a pattern or texture. You do not need to show a lot of detail on the drawing, just try to create a suggestion of a pattern. Patterns and texture can be produced most easily with pencils or pens. Computer programs can also be used for this. Try printing some of these and cutting them out to use on your drawings. Look around you for inspiration, (try bark rubbings). Apply the same techniques to different surfaces in your home to create different textures.

Fig. 1.39

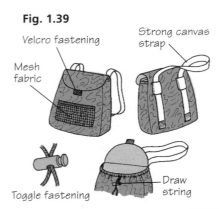
Velcro fastening
Strong canvas strap
Mesh fabric
Toggle fastening
Draw string

Experiment with a soft pencil, how many different textures can you create?

Look at a variety of fabrics, can you draw the effects created by the pattern?

Photocopy a sketch you have drawn, use different patterns and textures on each one to create a different effect.

Presenting work ➡

Try cutting out your final designs and pasting them on to a suitable background such as a piece of card called a mount. This gives sketches a more professional finish. There are two different ways of using a mount to display your design. The easiest way is to use a **flat mount**, this means that you glue your design on to a piece of card. You must take care to neaten the edges of your design. The other type of mount is a **window mount**. This is a piece of card with a hole (window) in it.

The design is fastened behind the window. First put your sketch on to a piece of card, then cut a hole in another piece of card. The window should be big enough to see the design, but not so big that you can see any untidy edges. Glue the card with the window in it over the sketch, taking care to cover any rough edges.

Try putting the picture on at an angle or group sketches of one item together. It is a good idea to include swatches of fabric which you would like to see used for your garment or product.

Fig. 1.40 *Texture and pattern*

Fig. 1.41 *Methods of presenting work*

Evaluating ideas

Evaluating ideas is the process of choosing the most suitable idea to develop further. Evaluating is a very important stage in the design process. At this stage careful evaluation will ensure that your design fulfils the criteria set out in the specification. It is very easy to stray away from the topic and design things which do not really meet your criteria if you do not evaluate your work carefully.

A simple way of beginning an evaluation of your ideas is to make a check list, like the one in Fig. 1.42 with your criteria from the specification across the top and the ideas down the side. Look at each idea in turn, if it conforms with the criteria tick the box; if it doesn't, put a cross in the box. This way you will be able to see which ideas are worth developing.

Ideas \ Specification	Product can be made in 6 lessons	Item is suitable for a baby of 8-12 months	Product has an educational value for baby	Product is between 400cm and 500cm in size	Item will not cost more than £5 to make	Item is safe	Item is washable
Wall hanging	✓	✓	✓	✓	✗	✓	✗
Soft-toy	✓	✓	✗	✗	✓	✓	✓
Play-mat	✓	✓	✓	✓	✓	✓	✓

Fig. 1.42

Ask yourself ...

Which of my ideas do I like the best?

Will my product harm anyone or anything?

Will my product be environmentally friendly?

Will my product look good?

Will I have to pay for the materials?

Will my product be expensive to make?

How will I finance my product?

Have I the ability to make my product or will I need help from other people?

Fig. 1.43 *Questions to ask yourself*

Choosing an idea

When you have completed your check list you must look very carefully at the ideas that match the criteria. You will need to ask yourself a number of questions about other things you may need to consider, which affect your work. Fig. 1.43 gives you some idea of the types of questions you may want to ask yourself.

Market research

If you are left with two or three ideas which all seem suitable it may be worth conducting some market research at this point. Ask people which of the ideas they prefer and why. Make a tally chart to show which idea has the most support. Remember that as a designer you are aiming to produce items which will appeal to a wide number of people in the market.

Compromise

Sometimes you may feel that one idea is the best, but it may, for example, be too expensive or take too long to make. At this stage you would have to **compromise** by deciding to develop the second best idea which is less expensive or quicker to manufacture.

When you have done this you will be able to choose one of the ideas for your product. The chosen idea is known as the **design proposal**.

Developing the chosen idea

Before you can begin to make your chosen item there are still many things which you will need to consider. This stage is known as developing the chosen idea and it is a very important part of the designing process.

Size and shape

For clothing you may need to collect information about average sizes. This is known as **anthropometric data**. Measurements should be taken from a number of people so that you can find an average size for the garment.

Aesthetic factors

Aesthetics depend on personal taste and are not as easily measured as other properties. A simple way of recording this is a star diagram or profile. Think of the attributes (characteristics) which you want in your fabric, such as softness, drape and brightness of colour. Then draw a star with a 'leg' for each attribute. (Star profiles can have any number of legs from 3 upwards.) Write the attribute you are testing at the end of each leg. Divide the legs into five point scales – use a ruler to measure accurately.

Repeat the process testing different fabric samples. This testing is sometimes called **attribute analysis**.

Testing the properties of fabrics

Flammability

When burned, some textiles give off fumes which are dangerous, others melt into plastic drops which stick to the skin, others will burn very quickly. Some fabrics can be treated with flame-proof finishes which affect how they burn. Making a wise choice of fabrics in some cases can save lives.

1. Attach the wire from each clamp, over the asbestos mat or sand box
2. Hang one length of fabric at a time over the wire
3. Pass the lighted Bunsen or splint close to the fabric and note what happens.

Record your detailed observations on a chart.

 Take care with this experiment. Never start the experiment without supervision.

Fig. 1.44 *Testing fabrics for sports clothing*

It will help you to decide which is the preferred fabric for the product.

Fabrics

At this stage you will need to test fabrics to ensure that they will provide the properties that your product requires. (Chapter 2 looks at fabrics and their properties.) It is a good idea to prepare any record charts which you may need before you begin testing. You may need to show why you chose your final fabric.

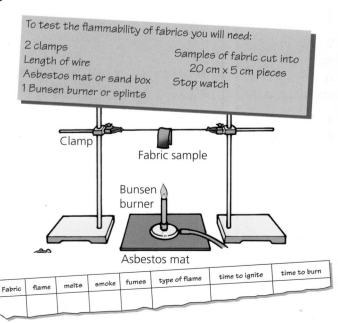

To test the flammability of fabrics you will need:

2 clamps
Length of wire
Asbestos mat or sand box
1 Bunsen burner or splints

Samples of fabric cut into 20 cm x 5 cm pieces
Stop watch

Fabric	flame	melts	smoke	fumes	type of flame	time to ignite	time to burn

Fig. 1.45 *Testing fabrics burning rate*

Insulation

Sometimes fabrics are needed to keep us warm. Air is a good insulator and for this reason it is sometimes trapped between fabric fibres or layers of fabric (as in quilting) to improve the insulating properties of the fabric. To test which fabrics are the best insulators try the following test.

1. To test insulation wrap a layer of each fabric sample around a boiling tube.
2. Boil some water.
3. Measure 25 ml of boiling water into each boiling tube.
4. Close each boiling tube with a bung.
5. Place the temperature sensors in the bungs, touching the water.
6. Set the datalogging program to run (see page 21).
7. Using the graph produced by the program decide which fabric has lost the least heat. This fabric is the best insulator.

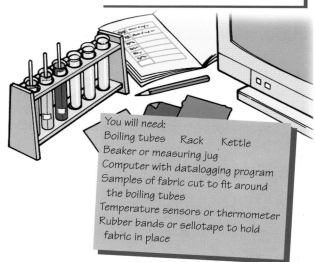

You will need:
Boiling tubes   Rack   Kettle
Beaker or measuring jug
Computer with datalogging program
Samples of fabric cut to fit around the boiling tubes
Temperature sensors or thermometer
Rubber bands or sellotape to hold fabric in place

Fig. 1.46 *Testing the insulation properties of fabrics*

Note: If you do not have datalogging equipment in school use thermometers in the boiling tubes. You will need to measure the temperature yourself at regular intervals.

Datalogging

Datalogging has many uses in textiles. It can be used to measure the amount of light which passes through fabrics which may be used for curtains or blinds. Can you work out how to do this using light sensors?

Elasticity

Some fabrics will loose their shape if they are stretched, others return to their shape quickly. Use this test to find out if your fabrics will spring back into shape.

You will need:
Strips of fabric,
  5 cm x 3 cm
Graph paper
Weights
Clamps
Wire or string
Pegs

1. Measure the fabric carefully.
2. Draw around the fabric onto graph paper – don't forget to label the diagrams.
3. Hang the strips of fabric over some wire or string stretched between two clamps.
4. Put equal weights on the bottom of each fabric. Leave for a day.
5. Remove the weights and the pieces of fabric and put them on to the graph paper over their original diagrams. Leave the fabrics for 30 minutes. Record which fabrics have returned to their original shape.

Fig. 1.47 *Ski-wear must be insulated but not absorbent*

Absorbency

Sometimes it is important for fabric to absorb moisture. Clothing worn close to the skin is more pleasant if moisture is absorbed. If the fabric does not absorb moisture we may feel 'sticky' in warm conditions. For some items such as ski wear, it is important that the outer layer of fabric is not absorbent. (Otherwise skiers would quickly become cold and wet.) To measure the absorbency of a fabric use this simple test.

You will need:
Tumble dryer
Hand hot water
Detergent
Pegs
Clothes line or string
Electric Balance
Fabric samples

1. Cut evenly sized samples of fabric
   5 cm x 5 cm is ideal.
2. Place the fabric samples in the tumble dryer for 5 minutes to make sure that they are thoroughly dry.
3. Cool and weigh each sample – record the weights on a chart.
4. Add detergent to the hand hot water and wash the samples for the same length of time.
5. Rinse and peg on a line (the line may be strung between two clamps).
6. Allow the fabrics to drip for 15 minutes.
7. Weigh the samples and record the weight. Note which fabrics retained the most moisture and which lost moisture quickly.

Stain resistance

Stain pieces of fabric which you are considering using for your product with things that are likely to be spilled on it. For example coffee or tea might spill on a table cloth, ink might leak on to a pencil case or make-up might spoil a shirt. Let the stain dry, then try to remove it using detergents or cleaning products that would be suitable for your product. Record your results on a 1–5 scale where a clearly visible stain would score 1 and a clean piece of fabric scores 5.

Durability ➡

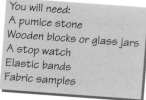

You will need:
A pumice stone
Wooden blocks or glass jars
A stop watch
Elastic bands
Fabric samples

Some fabrics are harder wearing than others. A simple test can be used which will help you to compare the durability of fabrics.

1. Stretch samples of fabric around a wooden block or over the neck of a jar, fasten in place with an elastic band.
2. Rub the pumice stone over the fabric in one direction only. Time how long it takes until the first hole appears.
3. Record your results in a table in order of durability. The fabric which took the longest time to form a hole will be at number one.

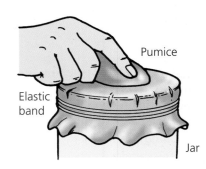

Fig. 1.48 Which fabric is the most durable?

Crease resistance

You will need:
Samples of fabric
Stop watch

The way a fabric creases can affect your final choice.
Some fabric is intended to look creased and this can be used as a feature of your design. However in other products (especially in products that cannot be ironed) creases can spoil your product.

1. Crease a piece of fabric in your hand, hold it for 10 seconds
2. Release the fabric

See if the fabric springs back quickly, or remains creased. Use a five point scale to record how creased the fabric is. Observe the fabric and record the results at one minute intervals for five minutes. Record the results in a table.

Time	Minutes				
Fabric	1	2	3	4	5
Cotton					
Silk					

Fig. 1.49 Results table

Washability

Some of the items you make will need to be washed frequently. It is important that they will still look good after several washes. To test this, cut four pieces of each fabric sample to the same size, 5 cm × 5 cm would do. Wash one piece of each fabric at 40°C, one at 65°C and one at 90°C. Dry and iron each piece. Keep one sample unwashed as a 'control'.

Use a chart to record your observations. Examine the fabrics for colour, size/shrinkage, creasing and pilling. Use the control to help you to do this. Give each piece a mark out of five for each of the tasks, add up the final score. Which fabric looks the best after several washes? Remember that you will need to include laundry instructions on each item you produce.

You may not be able to find a fabric which has all the properties you need that is within your budget. In this case you will have to **compromise** by using the fabric which provides most of the properties you need and which you can afford. Remember some properties may be essential. For example, flameproof fabrics must be used for children's pyjamas.

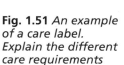

Fig. 1.51 An example of a care label. Explain the different care requirements

Fabric	temp	colour	size and shrinkage	creasing/ pilling	felting
cotton	40°c				
	65°c				
	90°c				
silk	40°c				

Fig. 1.50 Record chart

Developing ideas for decoration

Sometimes you will be required to develop a decoration for your product. Information on how to apply decorations to fabrics can be found in Chapter 2. It can be difficult to think of shapes, but lots of help can be found by looking around you. Collect pictures from nature – leaves, shells and flowers all have unusual shapes, or collect pictures from magazines or travel brochures.

1. Make a small cardboard frame and pass this over the picture until you find a section which you like.
2. Draw this area carefully.
3. Think about different ways of putting your image together, then try them out. Think about the tessellation you have done in maths!

Fig. 1.52 *Finding image*

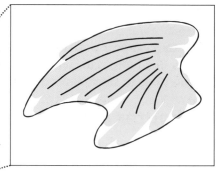

Fig. 1.53 *Draw the image you have chosen*

Fig. 1.54 *Tessellation*

Fig. 1.55 *Sometimes the internal shape can be used*

←Tessellation

By using different combinations of the image you have drawn you can begin to develop a new design. If you scan your image into the computer this part of the work will be quicker. This is a good use of computer aided design (CAD).

By repeating the image in this way you may find a design which you would like to use, or you may find a new design by placing your images together. In this case you may want to repeat the tessellation exercise with the new shape.

Repeats

If you are producing a simple stencil or piece of appliqué, the design you have made may be large enough to cover the required area of fabric. In some cases, however, you may need to repeat the design to cover a larger area. Experiment with the different methods of repeating the pattern to find the one that is best for the design. Information on pattern repeats can be found in chapter 2, on page 54.

Try to use a computer to help with this part of the work, it will be much quicker than drawing by hand. If you do not have access to a computer program which will allow you to do this, scan or photocopy your image and print it out several times. This way copies of your design can be cut and pasted to experiment with the pattern repeat.

Colour combinations

Once you have chosen your design repeat you will have to experiment with colours to find the best combinations. If the pattern is based on a particular theme try using colours associated with that theme. For example, a design that was inspired by China might use reds and golds as a starting point. If your work is based on natural themes choose more natural colours like greens and browns. If the image came from the sea, blues and greens could be used.

Use a computer to scan in the image and experiment with different colour combinations. If it is not possible to use a computer, photocopy the designs and colour them using coloured pencils. Don't forget to include all of these colour options in your final portfolio to show how you decided which colours to use.

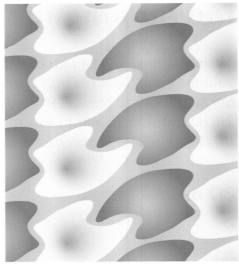

Fig. 1.56 *A colour combination*

Computer aided manufacture

If you have used the computer to help you design your shape or pattern, you may be able to use it to make the stencil for printing work, or to form a template to cut around for appliqué. Use a plotter-cutter to draw or cut out the pattern shape you need. This is one example of computer aided manufacture (CAM). If you cannot use a cutter, print out a copy of your stencil and carefully cut it out using a craft knife and mat.

Fig. 1.57 *Roland CAM*

Fig. 1.58 *Producing a sample*

 Be very careful when using a craft knife. If you are cutting straight edges always use a metal ruler as this will protect your fingers if the knife slips.

Developing techniques

Once you have decided on the design which you want to use it is a sensible idea to produce a sample. This could be made in paper first or from an inexpensive fabric such as lining. Producing a sample will allow you to practise your technique before you begin using expensive fabrics in your final product. In this way you can avoid costly mistakes and it will help you to produce your best work. Instructions for printing and appliqué can be found in Chapter 3.

Modelling

Modelling is an excellent way of developing your ideas A model is anything which gives an image or example of items in real life. There are two forms of modelling used in D&T, two dimensional (2D) modelling and three dimensional (3D) modelling.

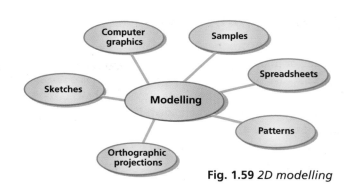

Fig. 1.59 *2D modelling*

2D modelling

Two dimensional modelling allows you to try out different ideas before you make final decisions. This helps you to avoid making costly mistakes. Any 2D method of communicating your ideas to another person is a form of modelling.

Patterns

The pattern pieces for any product are a form of 2D modelling.

Commercial (bought) patterns are available, these have been developed for a particular size and style. You may need to **modify** (change) a commercial pattern to suit your own design.

Fig. 1.60 *Tailor cutting round a marked pattern*

Block patterns are the basic pattern pieces which are used to make all garments. These are produced to fit the average figure in all sizes. You will need to amend the standard pattern shape to create your own shapes. Sometimes it will be necessary to make your own pattern pieces. In Fig. 1.61 you can see how one student coped with a design brief which required a pattern to be made.

Fig. 1.62 *Draw out the pieces you will need*

Fig. 1.63 *What measurements will you need to take? Check these carefully with a tape measure*

Brief

Design and make a hot water bottle cover. You will need to investigate the insulation properties of different fabrics and make your own pattern for the cover.

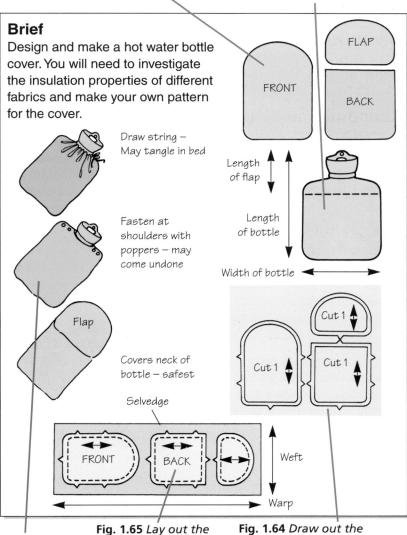

Draw string –
May tangle in bed

Fasten at shoulders with poppers – may come undone

Covers neck of bottle – safest

Fig. 1.61 *What type of fastening?*

Fig. 1.65 *Lay out the pattern pieces on the fabric, following the straight grain of the warp*

Fig. 1.64 *Draw out the pattern shapes on drafting paper – don't forget to add 1.5 cm for a seam allowance and notches for markings*

3D Modelling

Once you have produced your design ideas in 2D you will need to produce a 3D model, or 'mock-up'. Mock-ups may be done to scale or life size, depending on the cost and time involved. Scaled models are normally made to be one quarter life size. Textile designers often make full sized models of their garments in calico, which is an inexpensive fabric. This model is known as a **toile**. Garments are often fitted on a tailor's dummy. Many tailor's dummies can be adjusted to the measurements of the person for whom you are making the garment.

You can use paper, card, inexpensive fabric such as lining material or even dustbin liners or old carrier bags to produce a mock-up of your product. The mock-up allows you to test if the pattern works. It is also a simple way of working out the order in which you need to construct the item.

Once you have produced your 3D model you will be able to identify any problems. This will allow you to modify your work. You may need to produce another mock-up to include all of your changes. Keep all of your mock-ups, or if this is not possible take photographs of them. Using a digital camera will speed up this process. You will be able to use these photographs in your evaluation.

Fig. 1.66 *Fitting a toile on a tailor's dummy*

3D modelling:
- gives you a clear idea of how your product will look;
- highlights any problems you may have in construction;
- allows you to see if the product is in proportion;
- provides an opportunity to test and modify aspects of your work.

Computer modelling in industry

In industry, computers are used for a wide variety of modelling. They can be used to model different colours for garments or repeats of designs. They can be used to produce 2D models showing the way in which pattern pieces could be laid on to the fabric. This allows the manufacturer to work out the most economical layout plans for products, minimising wasting fabric keeping down costs of the product.

A number of computer programs allow 3D modelling to be used on the computer. It is possible to scan in pattern images and then use these scans to cover your model. This is very useful for large items such as sofas. The designer and client are able to see the finished effect without the expense of covering a large item with fabric.

It is also possible to produce moving images which show garments as they would look when they are worn – without the expense of setting up a fashion show.

Fig. 1.67 *Modelling on screen*

Prototypes

At this point you are ready to manufacture the item you have designed. In industry this is the point when prototypes are made. Prototypes are used to test the finished item. A number of products will be produced. They will be put through rigorous testing procedures to check that they do not fall apart when washed or cleaned and that they stand up to the wear and tear they were designed for. If the prototypes pass the tests successfully the product will go into full scale production.

Fashion shows

Fashion shows are used by designers to show their work, this allows them to see how people react to their designs. The work of some of our most famous designers is seen each year at fashion shows, and is used as a model for other designers to work from. Adapted designs appear in the major chain stores a few months later, modified to suit a large number of consumers.

Fig. **1.68** *Some catwalk designs can be adapted by high-street stores ...*

Fig. **1.69** *... But do you think this would be suitable?*

Planning

Planning is a very important part of the design process. Careful planning will enable you to turn your ideas into reality (realisation). Planning your work thoroughly will help to prevent you from making mistakes and wasting both materials and time. Planning can be divided into three main areas: **product** planning, **resource** planning and **action** planning.

What do I need to do?
What fabrics and materials do I need?
What equipment do I need?
Where will I get them from?
Do I need to practise any new skills?
How much time do I have to make it?
When do I need to have finished this?

Fig. 1.70 *Planning the product*

Product planning

Once you have formed your design proposals you will need to think very carefully about how you are going to make your product. Planning is important in your school work, but it is even more important in industry. The separate components could be made in different parts of the country and assembled somewhere else. This means that as much information as possible is needed to guarantee that the product looks the way it was planned. You may need to prepare **working drawings** of your product which other people can follow.

Pattern layout plans are used to show where the pattern pieces should be laid on the fabric. They will show any folds on the fabric, the grain and the selvedge. An arrow on the pattern piece will show how to align the pattern with the grain of the fabric. In industry computer programs are used to plan the pattern layout. This minimises the wastage of fabric in large scale manufacturing.

If a manufacturer is making 1000 items, by saving only 5 cm of fabric on each item they would save 50 m of fabric! How much money would be saved if the fabric cost £5.00 per metre?

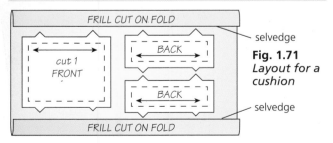

FRILL CUT ON FOLD

cut 1 FRONT

BACK

BACK

FRILL CUT ON FOLD

selvedge

selvedge

Fig. 1.71 *Layout for a cushion*

Sequential diagrams (step-by-step instructions) are used to show the order in which an item is assembled. Bought patterns usually have a sheet to show you how to assemble the item. You will need to produce a sequential diagram for your product.

Construction techniques

Test different types of seams and methods of neatening edges to help decide which is the best method of construction. This will also help you to develop skills in using the sewing machine or overlocker. Keep these examples of seams for future reference.

Once you have decided on the method of construction to be used, include a note to explain why you have chosen it. You will be able to refer back to this in your evaluation. What other techniques will you need to make decisions about?

Edges to be neatened

Flat seam neatened
Easy to sew
Will not take much strain, therefore may not be suitable for bag

French seam
Bulky inside bag

strain taken in both directions
Run = felled seam
seam
Neat finish
This is the seam I will use as it will take most strain and it looks neat

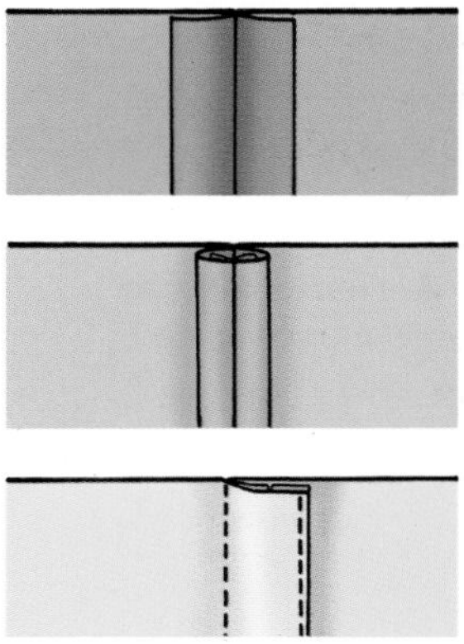

Fig. 1.72

Resource planning

Before you are ready to begin manufacturing, check that all the resources you need are available. Make a list of the equipment you will need, check the amounts of fabrics you are using. What else will be needed? Zips, buttons, threads and interfacing are called 'notions' or 'haberdashery'. Will any of these be needed?

Haberdashery
1 metre blue checked gingham
20 cm interfacing
15 cm blue zip
Blue cotton thread
Equipment
Pins   Needles
Sewing machine
Fabric scissors
Tailors chalk
Tape measure

Fig.1.73 *Check lists*

Action planning

Before starting to make the product you must plan what you are going to do. This will allow you to make best use of your time, energy and resources. Remember that some tasks will need to be completed before other tasks can be started.

Block diagrams ➡

Action planning requires you to be logical, you must work out what needs to be done and in what order. The simplest way to make a plan is in a block diagram. Fig 1.74 shows how to do this.

Fig. 1.74 *Block diagram for making a cushion*

Flow charts

The stages involved in making something can be shown as a **flow chart** like the one in Fig. 1.76. British Standards Institute symbols are used so that flow charts are understood by everyone.

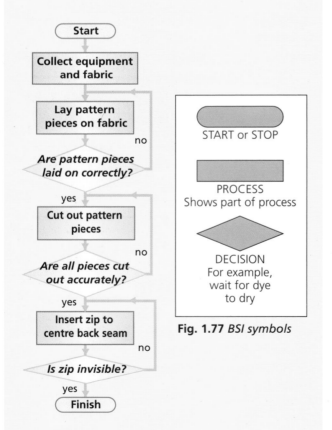

Fig. 1.76 *A flowchart for a cushion*

Fig. 1.77 *BSI symbols*

Time planning

Some projects will take several weeks to complete and you will need to plan ahead. Estimate how long it will take to complete each part of the process. A work plan for the whole term may be needed, this can be set out as a Gannt chart. Gannt charts are often used in industry for planning work schedules.

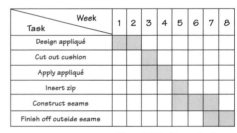

Fig. 1.75 *Gannt chart*

Quality Control

As you are working it is important to check the quality of the work to ensure that your product turns out the way you intended. Include quality control checks in your planning.

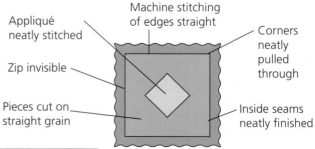

Fig. 1.78 *Quality control checks*

 Make sure that you have sufficient light before you begin working.

Making

*After you have planned your design proposal you are ready to turn it into reality (**realisation**). This is the making stage. Many people find this the most exciting and enjoyable part of their work.*

Be prepared

In most cases making the product will not be too difficult. If you have thought carefully about it and planned and prepared properly, then making the final product should be straight forward. You will need to have organised all your materials and equipment for the lesson and planned the order in which the pieces of the product should be joined together.

Before you begin

Check that you have all the items you need for the lesson. You may need to ask your teacher for help with techniques or equipment which are new to you.

Equipment

There are a number of pieces of equipment which you will need when you begin to make your product. These include the sewing machine, needles, tape measure, and sharp scissors. You will also need something to transfer pattern markings from the pattern to the fabric. A gauge is another useful item. This allows you to measure the correct seam allowance quickly all the way along the seam.

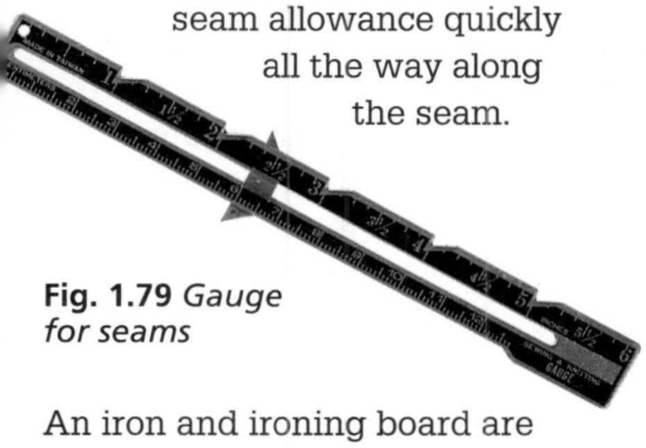

Fig. 1.79 *Gauge for seams*

An iron and ironing board are also essential items. It is important that the product is pressed at each stage of construction, this ensures a professional finish. A steam iron used with a pressing cloth will give the best results. In industry large pressing machines are used throughout the production process.

Work area

Try to keep your working area clear. Decide where you are keeping your small tools and equipment and always return them to this area. A small tray or tool box is a useful item for these. A tidy work area will help you to work more efficiently.

Fig. 1.80 *A tidy work area*

Aim for quality

Always aim to produce work of the highest quality. Be as accurate as you can when you are working with fabrics, measure carefully with a tape measure. Never cut out until your work has been checked by your teacher.

If you are not confident of your skill in a particular technique, practise it before using it in your project work.

Fig. 1.81 *Making a textile item*

> ⚠️ Always try to be aware of the dangers in a practical lesson and work as safely as possible. It is at this stage that accidents are likely to happen.
> - Never run in the room and take great care when handling hot irons or sharp tools.
> - Carry scissors with the blades facing down.
> - If you are passing scissors to other people offer them the handles, not the blades.
> - Keep the iron flex near to the wall and turn it off when it is not in use.
> - Keep your fingers well away from the machine needle and your forehead away from the thread carrier!

Evaluation and testing

Evaluation is a natural part of designing. It is unusual for a person to design and make a product without considering how successful it is. Very few people are completely satisfied with their work. Most people, if they are honest, will be able to suggest how they could improve their product. You may evaluate your work without realising it, when you reject some of your first ideas for example, or as you discuss your product with your friends.

Fig. 1.82 *A digital camera*

Evaluation as a starting point

Both in school and in industry evaluation of existing products can be used to begin to develop new ideas. You may be asked to look at different products and suggest how they could be improved.

Ongoing evaluation

It is easy to think that evaluation only takes place at the end of your work but this is not so. Ongoing, or progressive, evaluation takes place throughout the designing and making process. It is very important to evaluate your work as you progress. This will allow you to correct any mistakes or alter parts of your work which you are not satisfied with. Keep notes and sketches or photographs of your work as it progresses, these can be used when you write your final evaluation. A digital camera is a quick way of making a record of the stages of your work. Fig. 1.83 gives you some ideas of the questions you will need to consider as you make your textile product.

- Did I find any problems using the sewing machine?
- Do I need to ask for help with any of the techniques?
- Is the stiching straight?
- Are my seams finished neatly to prolong the life of my product?

Fig. 1.83

Admit mistakes

Try not to give vague answers like 'yes' or 'it looks fine'. Wherever possible give reasons for your answers. For example, '*My zip is not straight because I did not tack it in carefully before I machined it. I also forgot to change the foot to the zip foot. In future I will check that the zip is straight*

and carefully tacked before I use the machine and I will use a special zip foot.' It is important to be honest with yourself if you are to learn how to avoid making the same mistakes in the future. You will be credited with being able to evaluate your work fairly if you are honest.

Evaluating the finished product

You need to have something to judge your product against if your evaluation is to be useful. Think back to the specification. Do you remember how you thought carefully about the criteria that the finished product must satisfy? You can now evaluate your finished product against those criteria. Does your product fulfil all the criteria in the specification or just some of them? You may need to carry out tests to find out if you product works in the way you want it to. This is part of the **Quality Control** process.

Final evaluation

The records of the ongoing evaluation which you will have kept can be incorporated into the final evaluation. This will usually incorporate some testing of the product to find out if it does all the things you wanted it to do. For example, does a sports bag hold all of the items you need and is it strong enough?

Fig.1.84 *Does the product do what you wanted it to do?*

Testing the product

Testing can include a wide variety of activities, it may include **fabric testing**, and **user**, **product** and **safety testing**. Comparative tests for fabrics should have been carried out before you started manufacture (see page 20). Refer to them in your evaluation. Do you think you made the best choice of fabric now that the product is finished? Look at each of the statements in your specification. How can you test each one?

Specification	Control check	Tolerance	Monitoring	Corrective action
Pocket opens	Open and close the pocket 5 times	–	A button fell off	Remove buttons and replace firmly
Seams 1.5 cm	Use gauge to measure seam	±2 mm	Yes	–
The bag must hold all my sports equipment	Place items in the bag	–	Yes	–

User testing

It is a good idea to let the people who are going to use your product test it for you. For example if you have designed and made a sports bag let someone else use it for their sporting activities. This will allow you to record their reactions and suggestions for improvement.

User testing is often used in industry. Groups of potential users are asked to for their reactions and opinions about new products.

Product testing

The best way to test any product is to use it for what it is intended. Do not forget to keep a record of your findings as you use the product. How does it stand up to use? Does the sewing come undone? Do the fasteners work correctly over a period of time? Does the fabric wear well, even after washing?

In industry, once the design work is finished, a small number of products are produced for testing and evaluating. These are called **prototypes** and are designed to

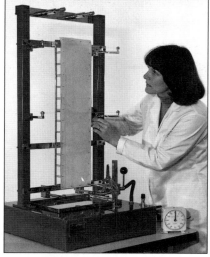

Fig. 1.85 *Testing of fabrics in industry*

be tested so that any faults or problems can be found before large numbers of the product are manufactured.

Safety testing

Designers have a responsibility to the people who use their products and to the environment. It is very important that what you design and make is safe to use. There are very strict rules and regulations which manufacturers in this country must follow. These are known as British Standards. Childrens' nightwear is one example of a type of product which must meet certain British Standards. The fabric used for children's nightwear must be non-flammable. This is carefully tested.

Overall evaluation

When you have completed your testing you will be able to make a final evaluation, this should include:

- How successful has your work been?
- What changes did you make as you were working, and why?
- Does your product look the way you wanted it to, if not, why not? How could it be improved?
- What changes would you make if you were starting this activity again, how would these changes improve the product?
- Did you plan your work in a way you could follow easily?
- Was your time management successful – how could you improve it?

Finally, try to look at the good points of your product. What are you particularly pleased with? What part of your design has worked well? Have you enjoyed your work? What have you learned through this activity?

2 INVESTIGATING TEXTILES

What are textiles?

Textiles is the name given to all fabrics. This includes fabrics which are woven and knitted; fabrics in one piece; and fabrics made into clothing or other items. Advances in technology have enabled fabrics to have a wide range of uses as in Fig. 2.1.

Fig. 2.1 *Textiles are very versatile – they can be used for everything, even to surround islands!*

Examining fabrics

All fabrics are made from **fibres**. Fibres are very fine, like hair. As fibres are not very strong, they are usually joined together to make a **yarn**. The yarn can then be combined to produce a mesh called **fabric**.

Fibres

All fibres come from either a natural source, or are synthetic. The names of some fibres and their origin can be seen in Fig. 2.3.

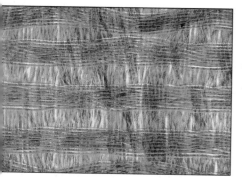

Fig. 2.2 *Fabric magnified to show its fibres*

These names are the **generic** names of the fibres (the general name given to fibres in that group). However, many manufacturers give their version of the fibre another name known as the **brand** name. Some examples are:

Generic name	Brand name
Elastane	Lycra®
Acrylic	Courtelle®
Polyester	Trevira®

Most fibres from natural sources are quite short in length. These are called **staple** fibres. Most manufactured fibres are made in continuous lengths. These are called **filament** fibres. Sometimes these filament fibres are cut up to produce shorter fibres, these are then spun into yarns.

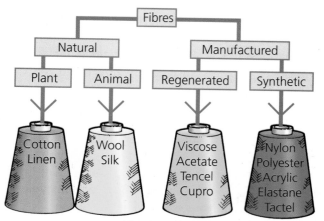

Fig. 2.3 *Fibres have many sources*

Yarns

Yarns are made by a process called spinning. Spinning twists fibres together to make a longer, thicker yarn which is much stronger than the fibre itself. The properties of the yarn can be changed by altering the amount of twist used when spinning fibres together. If fibres are twisted tightly, the yarn will be harder and stronger than a yarn made from loosely twisted fibres. The most common commercial spinning method allows fibres to be twisted together in either a clockwise direction, (which produces an S twist yarn) or in an anti-clockwise direction, (which produces a Z twist yarn).

The direction in which fibres are twisted together is important, S and Z twist yarns reflect light differently so a fabric made from single yarns would look 'patchy' if both types of yarn were used.

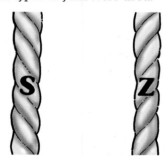

Fig. 2.4 *S and Z twist yarn*

A single yarn is often twisted together with another one or more yarns to make it even stronger and thicker. This type of yarn is called a **plied** yarn.

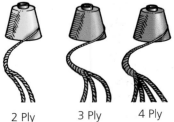

2 Ply   3 Ply   4 Ply

Fig. 2.5 *The most frequently used yarns*

Technologists have now developed yarns which are thinner than a piece of hair. These are called **microfibres**. The fabrics made from these yarns are very lightweight and have enabled manufacturers to produce sumptuous clothes from synthetic fibres.

Blends and mixtures

Sometimes different types of fibres or yarns are used together. This can be done in two ways.

1 Mix different fibres together before spinning into a yarn. This is called **blending**.
2 Mix different yarns before making a fabric. This is called **mixing**.

Blending and mixing fibres and yarns aims to:

■ improve the properties of a fabric – a fibre which is not very absorbent, such as polyester, can be blended with a fibre like cotton which is absorbent;

■ improve the look and feel, known as the **aesthetics** of a fabric – dull yarn such as cotton can be mixed with acetate or another shiny fibre;

■ control the cost – expensive fibres like lambswool can be blended with a cheaper alternative such as viscose.

Interesting yarns can be produced by twisting together two or more yarns which are different in some way. For example, one of the yarns could be metallic; a hard and soft yarn could be used together; two different coloured yarns could be used. There are many of these **fancy** yarns available. Fig 2.6 shows how some of these are made.

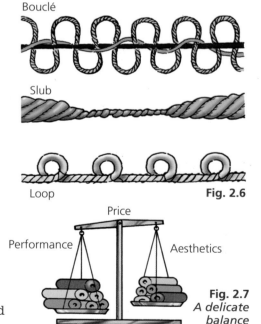

Bouclé

Slub

Loop   **Fig. 2.6**

The percentage of each type of fibre in the finished fabric has to be carefully balanced by the manufacturer in order to achieve the best possible performance, with the desired aesthetics at a sensible price.

Price

Performance   Aesthetics

Fig. 2.7 *A delicate balance*

1 Explain why yarns are usually plied.
2 Look at the labels in some of your clothes. Make a chart (see example below) which includes the name of the item, the fibres used and the reason for using those fibres.

Item of clothing	Fibres used	Reason
Shirt	Cotton/Polyester	dries quickly, absorbs moisture, easy to iron, cheaper than cotton

Choosing fabrics

Deciding what fabric to use when making a textile item is one of the most important decisions you will have to make. The fabric must be capable of doing the job intended – this is known as the fabric's **functional** properties.

Fig. 2.8 *Choose fabrics carefully!*

Fig. 2.9 *Deciding what fabric to use*

The **properties** of a fabric are affected by a range of factors. When choosing a fabric think about:
- what fibre/s have been used – have they been blended or mixed?
- How has the yarn been spun – loosely or tightly?
- How has the yarn been made into a fabric – was it woven, knitted or bonded?
- Have any special finishes been applied to the fabric?
- Has the fabric been coloured – have the yarns been dyed, or is the fabric itself printed or dyed?

Performance properties

These include the properties which affect how the fabric behaves when worn or cleaned.

Property	Importance
Absorbency	Does the fabric hold moisture?
Colourfastness	Does the dye in the fabric run when worn or washed?
Crease resistance	Does the fabric crease easily?
Durability	How long will the item last?
Flammability	How will the fabric react when burned?
Resilience (elasticity)	Does the fabric recover when it is stretched?
Strength	Is the fabric strong. Is it as strong when wet?

Aesthetic properties

These include the properties which affect how the fabric will feel and look.

Property	Importance
Appearance	How does the fabric look? Is it smooth, rough, flat, see – through?
Drape	How does the fabric hang? Is it stiff or soft?
Weight	Is the fabric light or heavy in weight?

Other properties to think about are:

Availability – it is no good deciding to make a waistcoat out of metallic fabric if your school or local shops don't have any.

Cost – choosing to make a waistcoat out of silk would be much more expensive than making it from polyester.

There might not be a fabric available which has all the properties needed, so a **compromise** will have to be made. In this case, a fabric which most closely fitted the properties needed would have to be used. See page 20 chapter 1.

One way to record the properties a fabric will need to have is to use a star profile. This makes it easy to see the importance of each of the properties in relation to the others.

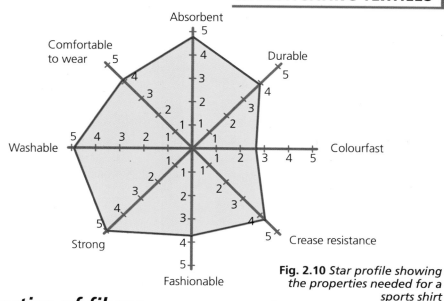

Fig. 2.10 *Star profile showing the properties needed for a sports shirt*

Comparing the properties of fibres

The properties of fibres have the greatest influence on the way a fabric will behave. The chart below compares the properties of different fibres.

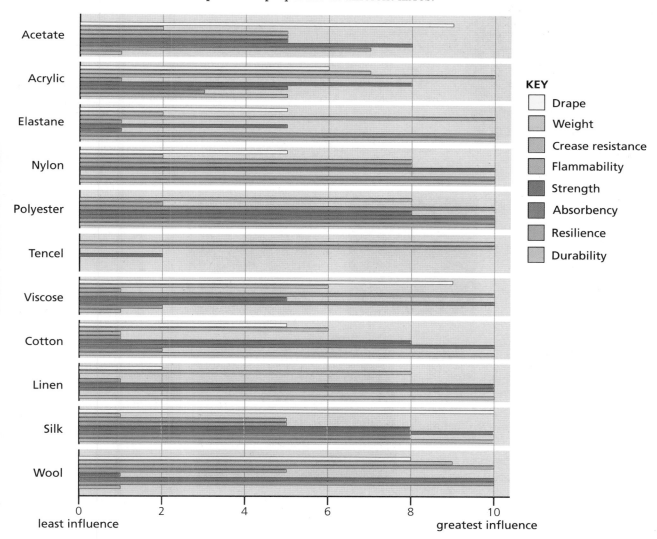

KEY
- ☐ Drape
- ☐ Weight
- ☐ Crease resistance
- ☐ Flammability
- ■ Strength
- ■ Absorbency
- ■ Resilience
- ☐ Durability

Making fabric

Fabrics are a mesh of yarns or fibres. There are lots of different ways of making this mesh. The method chosen depends on whether yarns or fibres are used. The way in which the fabric is made will influence the performance and aesthetic properties of the fabric. It is easy to look at the structure of a fabric using a hand held magnifying lens. Look carefully at how the fibres or yarns are held together. Are they interlaced, or looped, or matted?

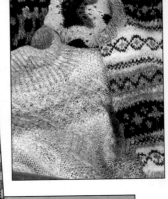
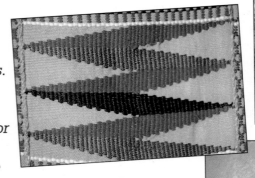

Fig. 2.11 *Woven, knitted and bonded fabrics.*

Making yarns using fibres

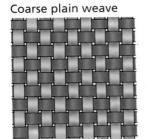

Weft ⟶

Warp

Selvedge

Fig. 2.12 *Weaving*

Both **woven** and **knitted** fabrics are made from yarns –

Woven fabrics

Woven fabrics are made by combining two yarns together using a **loom**. Many parallel yarns (called 'warp' yarns) run from top to bottom of the loom. Another yarn (the 'weft' yarn) crosses over and under the warp yarns. As the weft yarn wraps around each edge of the warp yarns, a **selvedge** is created. This makes an edge which does not fray.

By varying the way in which the yarns are interlaced, and how tightly the weft yarns are pushed together, different effects can be achieved. Some of these can be seen in Fig. 2.13.

Coarse plain weave   Fine plain weave   Twill   Herringbone

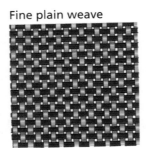
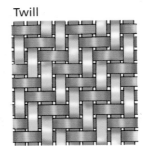

Fig. 2.13 *Different types of weave*

Looms can be very simple, as in Fig. 2.14. During the Industrial Revolution, looms which were driven by steam were developed to speed up the whole process. Today, woven fabrics are made commercially on very large looms which are computer controlled. Large quantities of fabric can be manufactured quickly to a set specification. This has made the process of weaving more reliable and efficient.

Fig. 2.14 *Weaving in India*
Fig. 2.15 *Computer-controlled loom*

More complex woven fabrics are created using a Jacquard Loom. This type of loom was invented by Joseph Marie Jacquard, a French man. The Jacquard Loom allows individual yarns to be selected at different times. This means that very complicated patterns can be woven.

The way a fabric has been woven – its **weave**, may affect the properties of the final fabric. A thick heavy weave will produce a fabric that is more durable than one made using a thin weave from the same type of fibre. A fabric which is tightly woven will be more durable than one which is loosely woven.

Woven fabrics are not stretchy, but will stretch diagonally across the weave (this is also known as the **bias**) of the fabric, – this property is useful when making bindings and facings to finish curved edges (see chapter 3 p 74).

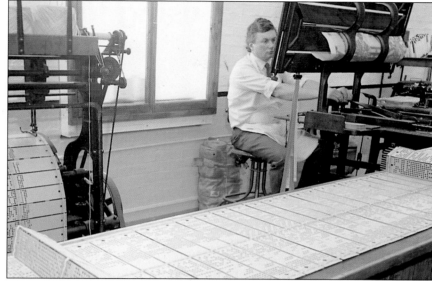

Fig. 2.16 *The Jaquard Loom uses cards like these to create complex patterns*

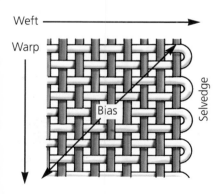

Fig. 2.17 *Bias*

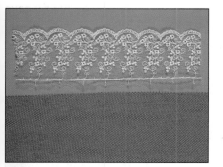

Fig. 2.19 *Lace and net.*

Knitted fabrics

Knitted fabrics are made by looping two or more yarns together. There are two main types of commercial knitting – **weft** knitting and **warp** knitting.

Weft knitting uses a continuous yarn to form interlocking loops across the width of the fabric. The fabric can be produced flat, or as a tube. This can be easily compared with hand knitting.

Warp knitting uses many vertical threads. These form loops which interlock with loops on alternate sides. This is a very quick way to produce fabric. Up to 2m of fabric can be produced in a minute!

Different types of yarns are often combined in warp knitting to produce fabrics which are stretchy. For example, elastane can be knitted with polyester to produce a durable, stretchy fabric suitable for swimwear.

Lace and **net** fabrics are also made using yarns. They are often warp knitted, but lace can also be made by knotting, braiding or stitching.

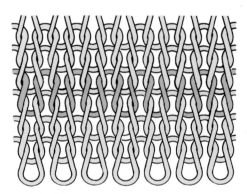

Weft knitting

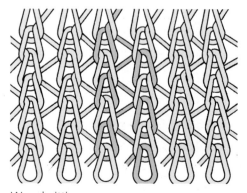

Warp knitting

Fig. 2.18 *Weft and warp knitting*

Properties of knitted fabrics	
Weft knit	**Warp knit**
Can easily unravel	Does not ladder
Frays easily	Does not fray
Ladders easily	Firmer than weft knit

Making fabrics using fibres

Fig. 2.20 *J-cloths and filters are made from non-woven fabrics*

*In these methods of fabric production, the process of making a yarn is missed out. Instead, fibres are bonded together, either using chemicals or by mechanical means to make a web called a **batt**. Fabrics made using this technique are often called **non-woven** fabrics.*

Once the web has been produced, it is held together by a process of needle punching, stitch bonding, adhesive (glue) bonding or thermal (heat) bonding.

Needle punching uses needles with barbs (hooks) on them which are pushed in and out of the fibres. This action makes the fibres lock together.

Stitch bonding uses lines of stitches to hold the web of fibres together.

Many blankets are made from needle-punched fabric. Stitch-bonded fabrics have a range of uses including luggage, industrial cloths, linings for footwear and mattress covers. Vilene, used for interfacing is an example of a fabric produced using adhesive bonding.

Fabrics made in these ways do not fray, they have no warp or weft and no bias or selvedge, therefore they are usually economical to use.

Fig. 2.21 *Felt products*

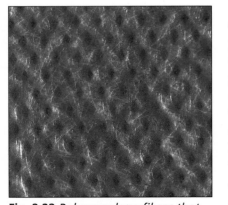

Fig. 2.22 *Polypropylene fibres that have been thermal-bonded*

Felt

Felt is a type of non-woven fabric. Traditionally, it was made by wetting then heating wool fibres. These were then moved so that the fibres rubbed against each other and 'locked' together to form a web of fibres. Commercially, felt is often made from other fibres such as viscose mixed with wool to produce a soft felt. This is usually strengthened using glue or by needle punching. This is a cheap, fast method of fabric production. Different textures and thicknesses of fabric can be achieved by altering the spacing and thickness of the fibre web.

When felt is steamed, it can be permanently pressed into a shape. This makes it a particularly good fabric for hats, which keep their shape even when wet.

Recycling fabrics

Fabric production uses a lot of energy and contributes to a wide range of environmental issues. These include potential pollution of the air, water and dealing with other waste products as a result of the manufacturing processes. Recycling fabrics instead of manufacturing from new raw products has a number of environmental benefits, including:

■ less energy being used;
■ less water being used;
■ less waste;
■ making fabrics from recycled plastic;
■ making use of old clothing which would otherwise have gone to landfill sites.

Fig. 2.23 *The easiest way to recycle fabric is to re-use it. These children are re-using clothes sent to them by a charity*

Many fibres, particularly synthetic ones do not decompose easily. It is very important that any fabrics produced from recycled fibres are of an acceptable quality to the consumer.

Fig. 2.24 *Clothes made by recycling fabric*

Laminated fabrics

The word 'laminate' means layers bonded together. This type of fabric therefore consists of two or more layers of fabrics applied to each other. The layers are usually held together by using either adhesive or heat. Stitching could also be used, as in quilted fabric.

Fabrics are laminated for a number of reasons:

■ Open weave fabrics, such as lace can be made more stable – this makes the fabric easier to work with and can reduce the manufacturing cost of making items as they are easier to machine.
■ A soft lining can be applied to prickly, rough fabrics, making them more comfortable.
■ Linings can be added to fabrics so that reversible styles can be manufactured. This is often seen in fabrics used to make jackets and coats.
■ The properties of the fabric can be altered. For example Goretex is a fabric produced by laminating a waterproof but porous layer between an outer layer and a lining. This has revolutionised outdoor sportswear, as the fabric prevents the wearer from getting wet if it is raining, but allows moisture created by the wearer to evaporate through the fabric, making it more comfortable to wear.

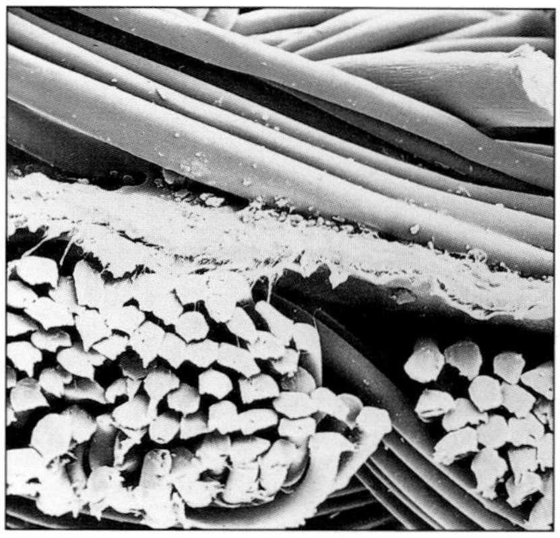

Fig. 2.25 *Layers in Gore-tex*

1 Investigate how the Industrial Revolution affected the production of woven fabrics.
2 Find two different woven fabrics. Describe their differences, and draw a diagram to show how each has been woven.
3 Look at the labels inside some knitted items to see what fibres have been used. Explain the properties these have which make them suitable for that item.
4 Compare a piece of Vilene interfacing with a piece of 'J' cloth. Try looking at each using a hand lens; do the fabrics stretch?. Try to pull the fabric apart – is one more difficult than the other?; Are the fibres different? Write about the differences you find.
5 Collect at least two examples of different laminated fabrics. What do you think these fabrics could be used for? Carefully take the layers apart. Describe how each layer has been manufactured – is it woven, knitted, or non-woven? What properties make these two fabrics suitable for their purpose?

Finishing fabrics

*Woven and knitted fabrics straight from the loom or knitting machine are called **grey goods**. It is quite common for further processing to take place before the fabrics are manufactured into products. These processes aim to improve the suitability of these fabrics by enhancing their aesthetic and performance properties.*

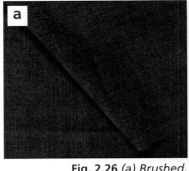

Fig. 2.26 *(a) Brushed, (b) mercerised, (c) moiré and (d) crêpe fabrics.*

A wide range of technological advances in this area mean that textile manufacturers can produce fabrics which can withstand the demands of users and are easy to care for.

There are three major reasons for applying finishes to fabrics. These are:
- To change the appearance of a fabric
- To change the handling properties of a fabric
- To improve the performance of a fabric in use.

Many of the finishes used will do more than one job, so the finishes under the headings below are listed according to the main jobs they do.

Changing the appearance of fabric

Brushing

A smooth fabric can have the surface brushed in order to make it feel and look fluffy. This process creates a **nap** on the fabric. Cotton, wool, and nylon fabrics can all be brushed by passing the fabric between rollers which have fine teeth attached to lift the surface of the fabric. Fabrics which have this finish applied need care when making into products. The nap lies in one direction, and therefore when cutting out a pattern all the pieces must run in the same direction. If not, the different pieces can appear to be different colours.

Mercerising

This process is carried out using chemicals. It makes the fibres more shiny, stronger, softer and increases their absorbency which can be useful when dyeing. The process is used on cotton yarns and fabrics.

Crêpe finish

This finish gives a rough, uneven surface. Yarns which have been tightly twisted are used, and these have heat and moisture applied. Viscose, wool and silk can have this finish applied. Many crêpe fabrics are likely to shrink, so care must be taken in choosing and caring for them.

Embossing

Embossing is used on synthetic fibres which are thermoplastic – this means that they can be set into shape using heat. These fibres have heat applied, and then they pass through engraved rollers which create the pattern. Fabrics with an embossed finish are not usually as durable as those with a crêpe finish.

Calendering

This process produces a smooth, lustrous fabric. It is achieved by passing fabric under pressure through heated rollers. By using fabric with a slightly ribbed appearance, a 'water mark' effect can be achieved. This type of fabric is called moiré. Fabrics which have this finish applied can often be stiff to handle.

Changing the handling qualities of fabric

Crease resistance

A crease resistant finish can be used with cotton and rayon fabrics. The fabric is treated with a resin and then heated. Fabrics treated in this way can often feel stiff.

Shrink resistance

Many fabrics including cotton and viscose are treated to prevent them shrinking when washed. The fabric is stretched along the warp whilst being woven or knitted. The fabric is then washed or damp pressed, which makes the fibres go back to their original size. Wool fabrics can be treated with resin or chemicals to make them shrink resistant.

Fig. 2.27 *Testing flame resistance*

Improving the performance of fabric

Flame resistance

This is often achieved with a spray-on finish which makes the fabric either resistant to the spread of flames, or difficult to ignite. It is a particularly important finish when considering using fabrics for nightwear and furniture. Cotton, linen and rayon fabrics can have this finish applied to them Fig. 2.27.

Stain resistance

Many fabrics can be treated with either silicone or resin in order to help them resist stains. It is important to read the labels of garments which have this treatment as care is needed when cleaning them.

Anti-static

This finish disperses static electricity so that fabrics are less clingy. It is often applied as a spray, usually to synthetic and silk fabrics.

Before finish water soaks into fabric

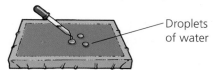

Fig. 2.28 *When a water repellent finish is used, water sits on the surface of the fabric*

Water repellence

A water repellent finish prevents drops of water being absorbed into the fabric which would make it wet. It is widely used on a range of fabrics including cotton. These fabrics are often called 'showerproof'.

Anti-pilling

The surface of wool and synthetic fabrics can be spoiled because they become covered with little bobbles. Solvents can be applied to these fabrics which will help to prevent this happening.

Fig. 2.29 *A swing ticket*

After finish water is repelled by finish

Droplets of water

Permanent pleating

As the name suggests, this finish sets pleats permanently into wool and wool/synthetic mixtures. It is achieved by using resins along the pleat and then using heat to press the pleat into position.

Fig. 2.30 *Permanent pleats*

Information about any finishes applied to fabrics can usually be found on swing tickets. These labels also advertise the finish for the manufacturer.

Natural fibres: animal

There are two types of fibres from animals – wool and silk. Wool is produced from a number of different animals including sheep, goats, rabbits and camels. Silk is made by the silkworm which spins a cocoon of very fine fibre around itself.

Fig. 2.31 *Woolen items*

Manufacture of yarns from animal fibres

The animal making the fibre is only the start of this process. The fibres need to be collected, cleaned and then spun into yarns before they can be used to make fabrics. Fig. 2.32 below shows the main stages involved.

Wool		Silk

1 Collecting

Fleece is shorn from sheep.

Larva of the bombyx mori moth feeds on Mulberry leaves, and spins cocoon around itself.

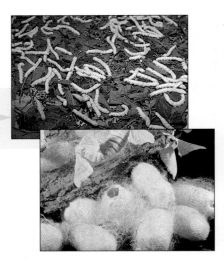

2 Cleaning

Wool scoured to remove dirt and grease.

Cocoons put into hot water to remove the gum which helps to hold the cocoon together.

3 Straightening Fibres/Reeling

Carding helps wool fibres to lie parallel to each other.

Reeling unwinds the filament from 3–8 cocoons at a time

Fig. 2.32

Properties of wool

Wool fibres are staple fibres. Look at the wool fibres under a microscope (see Fig. 2.34). The fibres are crimped (not straight), and each fibre is made up of overlapping scales. This structure gives wool many of its properties and problems! If wool is washed in hot water the scales overlap each other and lock together. This makes the fabric shrink and can also result in **felting** making the fabric feel quite hard.

Properties of silk

Silk fibres are the only natural filament fibre. Look at them under a microscope (Fig. 2.35). The fibres are long, straight and smooth. This structure gives silk its properties. The table below lists the properties of both wool and silk.

Fig. 2.33 *Silk scarves*

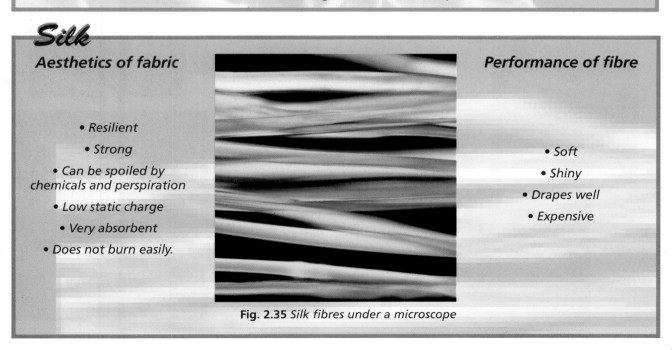

Wool

Aesthetics of fabric

- *Resilient*
- *Weak*
- *Absorbs moisture easily, but dries slowly*
- *Low static charge*
- *Does not burn easily*

Performance of fibre

- *Drapes well*
- *Creases drop out easily*
- *Soft*
- *Warm to wear*
- *Can be woven or knitted using thick and fine yarns to create a wide range of effects.*

Fig. 2.34 *Wool from an Angora goat under a microscope*

Silk

Aesthetics of fabric

- *Resilient*
- *Strong*
- *Can be spoiled by chemicals and perspiration*
- *Low static charge*
- *Very absorbent*
- *Does not burn easily.*

Performance of fibre

- *Soft*
- *Shiny*
- *Drapes well*
- *Expensive*

Fig. 2.35 *Silk fibres under a microscope*

Natural fibres: vegetable

There are two main vegetable fibres – cotton and linen, although other plants are also used. Jute is often used for sacks and bags. Hemp is being developed by technologists as it can be grown organically. It can be used for making jackets, rope, string and canvas. Manufacturers are investigating a wide range of other vegetable fibres which can be produced cheaply. These currently include banana, pineapple and ramie fibres.

Cotton is made from a plant which produces a cotton boll (this is the plants' seed case). The cotton plant is grown in warm humid climates. The climate affects the rate at which it grows. Bad weather can mean that less cotton is harvested, therefore the price of cotton increases.

Linen is made from the stem of the flax plant. It is an annual plant, (it needs to be sown every year) and is grown in temperate climates. The seeds of the flax plant can be harvested to produce linseed oil.

Manufacture of yarns from vegetable fibres

Once the plants have been harvested, the fibres need to be extracted, then cleaned and spun into yarn before making a fabric. Fig. 2.36 below outlines the main stages of this process.

Cotton

1 Collecting

Cotton is harvested using machines.

Linen

Linen is harvested using machines. **Retting** loosens the fibres from the outer stalk.

2 Cleaning

The fibres and seeds are separated using a process called **ginning**. Grit and other impurities are removed.

Seeds are removed from the stems. **Scutching** breaks up the stems to remove the fibres from the outer stem.

3 Straightening fibres

Carding makes the cotton fibres lie parallel to each other. As the fibres come off the carding machine, they look like a long rope called a **sliver**.

Fibres are put through a series of **combs** which remove the shorter fibres. These are used for cheaper fabrics.

Fig. 2.36

Properties of cotton

Cotton fibres are staple fibres. Look at cotton fibres under a microscope, and you will see that they look like twisted ribbons (Fig. 2.37). Cotton is one of the most versatile fibres – almost half of all textile products are made from cotton.

Properties of linen

Linen fibres are long staple fibres. Look at linen fibres under a microscope, you will see that they look like long tubes with marks along their length (Fig. 2.38).

Cotton

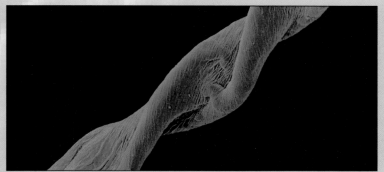

Aesthetics of fabric

- *Strong – and fibres are stronger when they are wet than dry. Therefore items made from cotton can be washed frequently*
- *Absorbs moisture easily making cotton fabrics easy to keep clean*
- *Conducts heat easily*
- *Damaged by sunlight*
- *Damaged by mildew. Therefore cotton textiles must be kept dry*
- *Can be treated with a range of finishes to improve its properties*
- *Can be blended and mixed with a variety of other fibres*
- *Can be coloured easily*
- *Has a low static charge*
- *Flammable*

Performance of fibre

- *Comfortable to wear because it conducts heat easily and absorbs moisture*
- *Soft*
- *Creases easily*
- *Range of different effects can be created by using yarns of different thickness, and by choosing different weaves or knits to make the fabric*

Fig. 2.37 *A cotton fibre under a microscope*

Linen

Aesthetics of fabric

- *Is very strong when wet and when dry, therefore linen fabrics can be washed frequently*
- *Can withstand high temperatures*
- *Absorbs moisture easily*
- *Has a low static charge*
- *Can be blended and mixed with a variety of other fibres*
- *Flammable*

Fig. 2.38 *Linen fibre under a microscope*

Performance of fibre

- *Creases very easily*
- *Cool to wear because it absorbs moisture easily, but quickly disperses this back into the atmosphere*
- *Has a lustrous (shiny) appearance*
- *Is quite stiff*

Manufactured fibres

The manufactured fibre industry developed because people wanted to find a cheap way of producing a fibre that looked and behaved like silk. It was only just over 100 years ago that the first manufactured fibres were developed. The production of manufactured fibres can be controlled to make sure that fibres of the same thickness and quality are always produced.

There are two groups of manufactured fibres – regenerated and synthetic. Regenerated fibres are manufactured using a natural source as the starting point. Synthetic fibres are produced using chemicals obtained from coal and petroleum.

Production methods

Manufacturing processes used for both regenerated and synthetic fibres are very similar.

A liquid is produced in readiness for spinning. This means that the method of spinning is quite different from those used for the natural fibres.

The first stage of this process is to force (extrude) the thick liquid (polymer) through a spinneret (see Fig. 2.39). This produces many fine streams of fibres which are then solidified to form filaments.

Finishes can be applied to the fibre in its liquid form or later in the process.

There are three main types of spinning used for manufactured fibres – wet spinning, dry spinning and melt spinning.

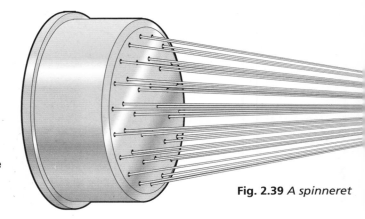

Fig. 2.39 *A spinneret*

Wet spinning

This involves extruding the liquid through a 'chemical bath' to solidify the filaments. This method of spinning is used in the production of viscose.

Dry spinning

During this process the liquid is extruded through warm dry air. The warm air makes any solvent used in the liquid evaporate, and solidifies the filament. This system is used in the production of acetate.

Melt spinning

This involves melting the solid polymer, then extruding it through cold air to solidify the filament. Melt spinning is used in the production of nylon and polyester. The filaments obtained are then stretched to improve their strength. This process is called **drawing**.

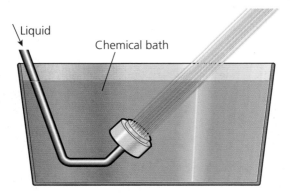

Fig. 2.40 *Wet spinning*

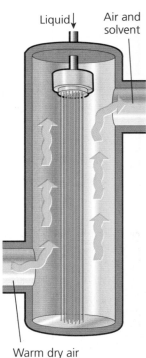

Fig. 2.41 *Dry spinning*

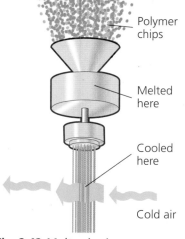

Polymer chips

Melted here

Cooled here

Cold air

Fig. 2.42 *Melt spinning*

Filaments obtained from any of these three process can then be spun together to make yarns of different thickness.

There are many techniques used to improve the properties of manufactured fibres and yarns. These include:

- cutting up the filaments to make a staple fibre. This can make fabrics made from these fibres warmer as air is trapped between the fibres;
- adding finishes to fibres in their liquid form including dye and flame-retardant chemicals;
- adding texture to the yarns using a process called bulking. This can make the yarns more absorbent, make them warmer and, in some cases, make them stretchy.

Regenerated fibres

Natural fibres are generally quite expensive to produce. Regenerated fibres were developed in an attempt to produce fibres more cheaply. The word 'regenerate' means 'form again'. Cellulose from cotton waste or wood pulp is used as it is quite cheap and it is a renewable resource. The cellulose is mixed with chemicals which change its structure. The result is a thick liquid (polymer) which can then be spun.

Viscose

Aesthetics of fabric
- Soft
- Creases easily
- Inexpensive
- Drapes well
- Smooth

Viscose was the first regenerated fibre. The fibre is obtained by mixing cellulose from wood, then wet spinning the liquid. The wood is from sustainable forests and the solvent used is non-toxic. The solvent is continually recycled, making this an environmentally friendly fibre. The generic name for fibres made in this way is Lyocell. Recent advances in technology have resulted in the development of the first new fibre for 30 years, called Tencel®.

Performance of fibre
- Absorbent
- Strong – but not quite as strong as cotton
- Washes easily as fibres shed dirt
- Can be dyed easily
- Not very elastic
- Fibres are likely to shrink
- Has a low static charge
- Flammable
- Can be mixed with other fibres

Modal

Aesthetics of fabric
- Soft
- Inexpensive
- Drapes well
- Smooth

Modal is manufactured in a similar way to viscose. However, the fibres produced are stronger, and this fibre is the closest to having the properties of cotton.

Performance of fibre
- Strong when wet or dry
- Absorbent
- Has a low static charge
- Can be mercerized. (made shiny)
- Often mixed with other fibres such as polyester and cotton
- Flammable

Acetate

Aesthetics of fabric
- Crease resistant
- Lustrous – acetate fabrics are often used for linings in clothes
- Smooth
- Drapes well

Acetate is manufactured from cellulose obtained from wood pulp. The liquid is dry spun, which is quicker and cheaper than wet spinning.

Performance of fibre
- Weak
- Elastic, therefore fabric does not crease as easily as viscose.
- Not absorbent
- Difficult to dye
- Flammable
- Affected by some solvents – particularly acetone which will dissolve the fibre very quickly
- Can be mixed with other fibres
- Thermoplastic – this means that fibres can be set into shape using heat. Used for setting pleats and creases in clothing

Synthetic fibres

Synthetic fibres are produced from chemicals obtained from coal or petroleum. Nylon was the first synthetic fibre. It was invented in 1935 by an American chemist called Wallace Hume Carothers. Polyester, acrylic and elastane are the other main types of synthetic fibres. Other manufactured fibres include metallic fibres such as Lurex®, glass fibre and PVC.

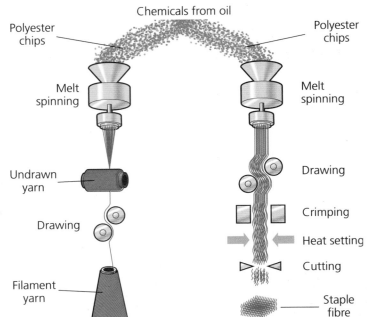

Fig. 2.43 *Polyester can be either a filament or a staple fibre*

Nylon

Aesthetics of fabric

- Crease resistant
- Uncomfortable to wear, because it does not absorb moisture
- Can cling
- Cheap
- Doesn't drape well
- Lightweight

Nylon (also called polyamide) is usually made from oil. The polymer is melt spun to produce yarns which can be woven or knitted.

Examples of nylon fibres include Tactel®, Celon®, Perlon® and Bri-Nylon®.

Performance of fibre

- *Very strong*
- *Very elastic*
- *Resilient*
- *Does not absorb moisture*
- *Easy to wash*
- *Thermoplastic, so can be permanently pleated and embossed*
- *High static charge, which can make clothes cling*
- *Melts, does not flare, therefore has low flammability*
- *Can be mixed with other fibres.*

Elastane

Aesthetics of fabric

- Light
- Usually mixed with other fibres to make fabrics stretchy and comfortable to wear

Elastane is manufactured from polyurethane. It is able to stretch up to 600% of its length before breaking. It is often mixed with other fabrics which need the ability to stretch, for products such as underwear, swimwear and sports clothing. Elastane is called spandex in the USA. Lycra® is the most common name for fabrics made from these fibres.

Performance of fibre

- *Very stretchy*
- *Resilient and therefore fibres recover quickly from stretching and creasing*
- *Usually blended with other fibres because of ability to stretch*
- *Can be washed easily*
- *Resists perspiration and body lotions*

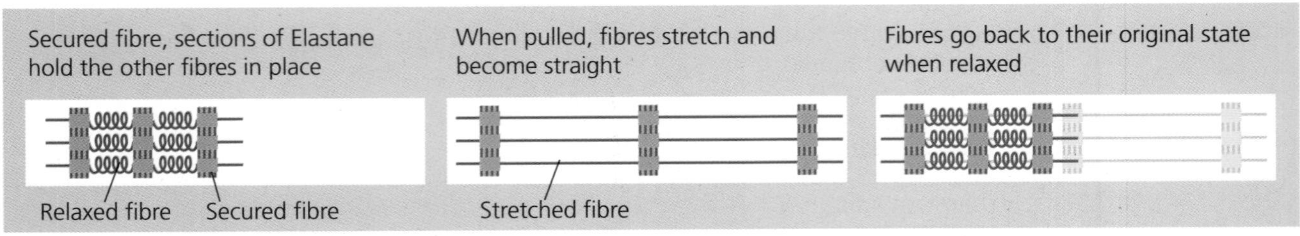

Secured fibre, sections of Elastane hold the other fibres in place

When pulled, fibres stretch and become straight

Fibres go back to their original state when relaxed

Relaxed fibre   Secured fibre

Stretched fibre

Fig. 2.44 *Elastane without tension, under tension and recovering from tension*

Acrylic

Aesthetics of fabric

- Crease resistant
- Uncomfortable to wear, because it does not absorb moisture
- Can cling
- Cheap
- Doesn't drape well
- Lightweight

Acrylic is made from a chemical called acrylonitrile which is derived from oil. It is either wet or dry spun, producing either staple or filament fibres. As a staple fibre, it has many of the properties of wool. Many different brands of acrylic fibre are produced. Examples include Courtelle®, Acrilan® and Orlon®.

Performance of fibre

- Can be bulked, this makes fibres trap air and so they feel like wool
- Poor conductor of heat
- Thermoplastic
- Can stretch in warm, moist conditions, therefore needs careful washing
- Not particularly strong
- Flammable
- Can be mixed with other fibres
- Need special dyes

Polyester

Aesthetics of fabric

- Does not crease
- Uncomfortable to wear, because it does not absorb moisture
- Can cling
- Cheap

Polyester is a very versatile synthetic fibre. It is made from chemicals derived from oil. The liquid is melt spun, then made into either staple or filament fibres. Fig 2.43 shows this process. Examples of polyester fibres include Terylene®, Dacron® and Trevira®.

Performance of fibre

- Very strong
- Fibre resists abrasion
- Very resilient – quickly recovers from creasing
- Not very elastic
- Easy to wash
- Has a high static charge
- Not affected by sunlight, making it suitable for making net curtains
- Thermoplastic
- Has a tendency to 'pill' (see p.41)
- Needs special dyes
- Melts, does not flare, therefore has low flammability
- Can be mixed with other fibres

New fibres

Manufacturers are constantly researching to find other sources for fibres which complement those already developed. Their aims are to develop fibres with improved or specific properties; to produce fibres which are not expensive; to develop environmentally friendly fibres. Developments include using metal and glass, developing light sensitive dyes, and producing **microfibres**. Microfibres are very fine fibres usually made from polyester. They can be blended with other fibres and because they are so fine, they can be woven very tightly making them waterproof. Fabric made from microfibres is lightweight, comfortable to wear and very durable.

1 Look at labels from three different items of clothing. What fibres have been used. Why do you think these are suitable? Are there any disadvantages of using these fibres?

2 Look at the photos in Fig. 2.45. For each item, state what properties are needed, and which fibres could be used.

3 What are the advantages of blending wool and polyester; cotton and polyester; cotton and elastane. For each blend, suggest two items which can be made.

Fig. 2.45 *Synthetic fabrics have useful properties*

Colouring fabrics

Consumers want fabrics that are attractive, easy to care for and hard wearing. Most fibres are either white or creamy in colour in their natural state. Therefore an important stage in the manufacture of fabrics is to add colour.

There are two ways to add colour to fabrics – **dyeing** and **printing**. Dyeing involves immersing the fibre, yarn or fabric into water containing the dye. Printing allows colour to be applied to the surface of the fabric.

Dyeing

All dyes are coloured substances which can be absorbed and retained by fibres. Traditionally, dyes were obtained from natural sources such as plants and minerals. Lichen, heather, beetroot, beetles and even shellfish have been used as dyes! However, these do not always produce a standard colour. Technologists discovered that many of the manufactured fibres could not be dyed using traditional dyes – either because the fibres did not take up the dye very well and were pale, or because the dye was not colourfast – that is, it washed out of the fabric. Many dyes are now manufactured from chemicals. Commercial dyeing uses huge quantities of water and produces waste products which are not biodegradable. Therefore new techniques are being developed which are more environmentally friendly.

1. *Mix dye with water*

2. *Add item to be dyed*

3. *Apply heat and sometimes pressure*

4. *Leave*

Fig. 2.46 *Stages of dyeing*

Whatever the source of the dye it must:
- have an intense colour;
- be soluble in water;
- be capable of being absorbed and retained by the fibre;
- be colourfast so that the dye does not run or wash out;
- not damage the fabric.

A chemical called a **mordant** is added to fibres which do not take up dye easily. It combines with the dye so that the fibres can absorb colour more easily. The mordant also helps to make dyed fibres colourfast.

⚠️ Be careful! Mordants are corrosive and toxic!

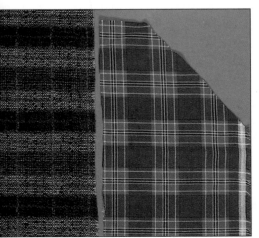

Dyeing can be carried out at one of three stages.
1 The fibres can be dyed. This can be before they are spun into yarn, or at the liquid stage in the case of manufactured fibres. This gives an good even colour, and usually results in better colourfastness.
2 The yarn can be dyed. The colour may not be quite as even as when dyed at the fibre stage.
3 The fabric can be dyed. This is often known as piece dyeing. This will give a fairly even colour across the whole length of the fabric.

Once dyed, there are almost endless possibilities for making attractive fabrics. Fibres of different colours can be spun together to make a multi-coloured yarn. When knitted or woven, the fabric will have a subtle mix of colours.

Fig. 2.47 *Tweed and checked fabrics*

Different coloured yarns can be woven together to make checked fabrics.

When different types of yarns such as cotton and polyester are used to make a fabric which is then piece dyed, the two fibres will react differently to the dye. This is called cross dyeing and it produces striped and checked fabrics.

Resist dyeing

The name of this process comes from the way in which the fabric is dyed. Certain parts of the fabric are protected from the dye by using wax, gutta or thread. The parts of the fabric protected remain the original colour.

There are three main types of resist dye – tie dye, tritik, and batik.

Tie dye

Tie dyeing relies on folding and tying fabric before immersing it in dye. By folding and tying the fabric in different ways, a wide number of effects can be achieved. It is important that the thread is tied very tightly to prevent the dye soaking into the fabric.

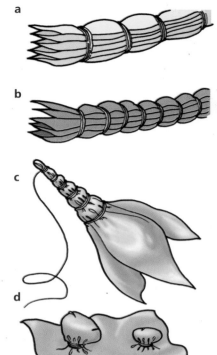

a

b

c

d

The fabric can be pleated, then thread wrapped at intervals along the pleat (see **a**). Dye the fabric. Wrap more thread around the newly dyed parts then dye with a different colour (see **b**).

Circular effects are created by firstly holding the fabric with your fingers in the centre, then pulling with the other hand to make a cone shape. Now threads can be tied at intervals along the length of the fabric (see **c**).

Objects such as pebbles or rope can be tied into the fabric. Wrap the thread over the fabric containing the object before putting into the dye (see **d**).

Tip: – leave a long thread so it is easy to get the fabric in and out of the dye pot.

Fig. 2.48 *How to prepare fabric for tie dyeing*

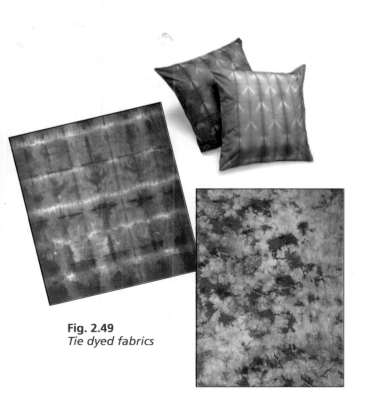

Fig. 2.49
Tie dyed fabrics

Note:

If you are planning to use more than one colour, always begin with the lightest colour. Think about how the second colour will affect the first colour. For example, if you use yellow, then blue, the result will be an area of green.

Tritik

Tritik is a form of tie dyeing which uses stitching rather than wrapping threads to resist the dye. The name comes form a Malayan word which means droplet.

The fabric can be pleated or folded before stitching. It is easier to keep some control of the pattern using tritik as you can decide exactly where to stitch.

Fig. 2.50 *Traditional batik fabrics*

Fig. 2.51 *Using hot wax*

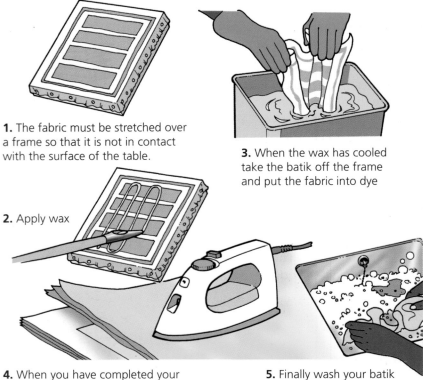

1. The fabric must be stretched over a frame so that it is not in contact with the surface of the table.

2. Apply wax

3. When the wax has cooled take the batik off the frame and put the fabric into dye

4. When you have completed your design iron the batik between sheets of absorbent paper

5. Finally wash your batik

Fig. 2.52 *Stages in batik*

Batik

This is an ancient method of applying colour to fabric. Fabrics from India, China, Japan and Africa are often coloured using this technique. It relies on using wax to prevent the dye from soaking into the fabric. Traditionally hot liquid wax was used for batik. More recently a wax has been developed which does not need to be heated. This 'cold wax' is much safer to use than traditional batik methods. Hot wax will crack when the fabric is in the dye, allowing thin lines of fabric to be dyed. This gives batik its characteristic appearance which is called marbling.

Hot wax is applied using a special

 Hot wax can burn, wear protective clothing and cover surfaces!

tool known as a tjanting. This consists of a small bowl to hold the wax with a spout through which the wax is poured.

The wax must be hot enough to soak in to the fabric and prevent the dye entering the fibres. If it is too cool, the dye will seep under the wax coating. To check if the wax is hot enough put a spot on a corner of the fabric. If it goes grey it is ready for use, if it remains white it is too cool.

The tjanting should be kept in the hot wax until it is needed so that the wax flows freely.

Move the tjanting over the fabric to make a pattern with the wax. Remember the areas covered with the wax will not take the dye. Immerse the fabric in the dye. Dry the fabric. This can be quickly done at school by using a hairdryer. Don't use too much heat or the wax could melt. Now

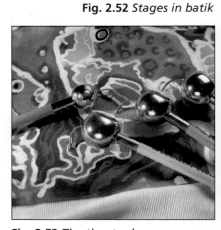
Fig. 2.53 *Tjanting tools*

apply more wax onto the parts you want to keep in this colour. Keep repeating the dyeing, drying and waxing until you have completed your fabric.

When you have completed your fabric, scrape the wax away from the surface, then sandwich the fabric between several sheets of absorbent paper, and iron with a hot iron until all the wax has gone.

Finally wash the fabric before use.

Silk painting

This is another type of resist dyeing. The dyes used (often called silk paints) have been specially developed to be watery enough to travel along the fibres quickly. They are very bright and can be mixed to make other colours. Metallic paints are also available.

The resist used in silk painting is called **gutta**. It can be bought in small bottles which have a fine nozzle attached. If you don't want to be left with white lines on the finished item use coloured gutta, which is also available in gold and silver. You could also begin by dyeing the whole piece of fabric a light colour first.

The gutta must penetrate the silk or the paint will 'bleed' (run into another colour).

Interesting effects can be created by sprinkling salt onto the surface of the fabric whilst it is still damp (Fig. 2.53).

If areas of the fabric are moistened before applying the paint, the colour will be much softer. It is also possible to brush over the surface of a ready painted area with a wet brush to remove paint. Experiment to see what effects can be created.

1. Put silk on frame

2. Outline your design with gutta
To check there are no breaks in the gutta – hold up to light

3. Use a brush to paint on dyes – work quickly before paint dries

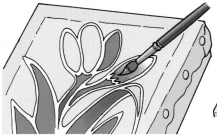

4. Dry fabric Remove gutta and fix the paint

Fig. 2.54 *Stages in silk painting*

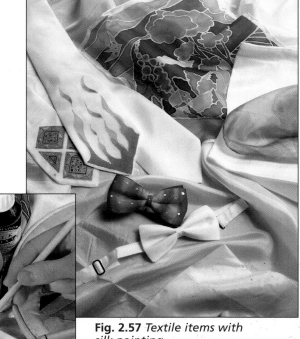

Fig. 2.57 *Textile items with silk painting*

If you are planning to include some silk painting on a textile item, it is best to plan to do this before making the item as the fabric can be more easily handled in a flat piece.

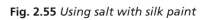

Fig. 2.55 *Using salt with silk paint*

Fig. 2.56 *Silk painting*

Printing

There are many different ways of printing colour onto the surface of fabrics. Some of these require specialised equipment, others can be done very quickly. Whatever method of printing you choose, you must make sure that the dyes or inks are suitable for the fabric you are using.

It is important to plan the design carefully before beginning to print onto the fabric. You also need to think about how the pattern will be repeated along the whole width and length of the fabric. Fig. 2.55. shows different ways in which patterns can be repeated. It is possible to try out different pattern repeats and colour ways using computer programs. These can save a lot of time, and help to avoid wasting expensive materials.

Block printing

This is one of the oldest ways of printing designs onto fabrics. The earliest examples date from the 5th and 6th century from Egypt. Blocks of wood were carved using chisels and knives. The cut surfaces were coated with dye. The block was then pressed onto the fabric, leaving an imprint of the pattern.

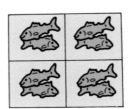  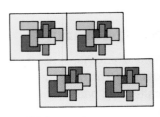

Full drop repeat   Half drop repeat   Brick repeat

Fig. 2.58 *Patterns can be repeated in different ways*

Fig. 2.60

Other materials can be used for making blocks. These include lino, corks, polystyrene food trays, empty cotton reels, sponges and even potato!

Designs for block printing can be created on a computer, and either printed out to make a pattern to help cut the block, or directly cut out of lino using a CNC miller.

Try experimenting with items like fern and leaves as blocks. These can be glued onto waste wood or thick card to make them easier to work with. The dye can be applied using either a brush or a roller.

Roller printing

This is a development of the principles of block printing. Designs are engraved onto copper rollers. Each colour to be used has a separate roller. The rollers pick up colour from a dye bath and transfer this onto fabric. It is a quick method for printing large quantities of fabric. It also enables different colourways to be created simply by changing the dye for a roller. It is not good for fine detail.

Fig. 2.61 *Roller printing*

Fig. 2.59 *Printing fabric with blocks*

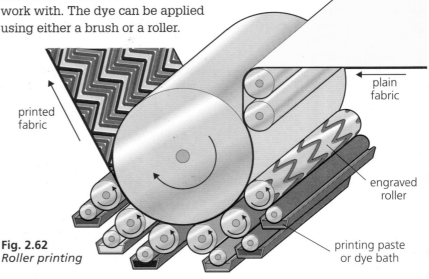

printed fabric

plain fabric

engraved roller

printing paste or dye bath

Fig. 2.62 *Roller printing*

Stencil printing

This is a quick, cheap form of printing. The earliest known stencils were used by the Japanese in the eighth century. Stencilling involves cutting patterns out of waxed paper, then dye is pressed through the holes onto the fabric. Stencils can also be made out of thin card, paper and sticky transparent film which can be stuck down onto the fabric, reducing the possibility of the colour 'bleeding'. A different stencil needs to be made for each colour used. Stencil designs are usually quite bold in shape – fine detail is difficult to achieve. Patterns can be created and printed on a computer ready for cutting out. A computer controlled cutter plotter such as the one in Fig. 2.64 could be used to cut out the pattern.

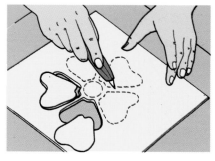

1. Cutting out stencil

2. Dye is pressed through the stencil

3. Finished article

Fig. 2.63 *Stencil printing*

Fig. 2.64 *Photo of CAMM1 with stencil coming off*

Screen printing

This is a development of stencil printing. Frames which were traditionally covered in silk are used (hence this technique is often called silk screen printing). The fabric has a template placed onto it, then the screen is placed on top. The dye is forced through the fabric using a squeegee. (A squeegee is a piece of stiff rubber held on a handle.) A different screen needs to be used for each colour.

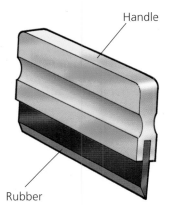

Handle

Rubber

Fig. 2.65 *A squeegee*

This process causes problems for printing large quantities of fabric because:
- the length of fabric which can be printed is limited by the size of frame;
- it is a relatively slow process;
- each screen can only be used for one colour.

However, the process can be simplified a little to make it possible to carry out in school.

Experiment with flat natural objects – flower petals or ferns make interesting stencils. A range of effects can be created very quickly. This process is described in detail on the next page.

Fig. 2.66 *Stages of screen printing*

The frame can be covered with nylon or polyester fabric which is much cheaper than silk. It is important that the fabric is stretched very tightly over the frame. The fabric used on the frame must be fine enough to allow the dye to pass through it. Polyester organdie is frequently used.

Cut out the design. Save cut pieces – you may need to cover printed areas if you are using more than one colour.

Place the fabric onto a padded surface. This can quickly be created by laying several sheets of newspaper on a table then cover with plastic sheet. Stick the edges down with masking tape. Place the stencil onto the fabric. Note: If you have used adhesive film for the stencil, this can be stuck directly onto the bottom of the screen.

Put the printing paste along one edge of the frame. The amount of paste to use depends on the area which needs to be printed. Don't use too much as this is wasteful.

Ask someone to hold the frame firmly. Hold the squeegee at 45°, drag the squeegee towards you evenly pressing the dye through onto the fabric.

VERY CAREFULLY remove the frame. Scrape out any paste from the frame. If you are going to use another colour, wash the squeegee and frame in cold water and dry well. Make sure that the first colour has dried thoroughly before adding another. A hair dryer is useful for drying the frame and fabric.

Fig. 2.67 *Screen printed fabric in single and multiple colours*

Transfer printing

This is a relatively new method of printing used in industry. It uses a process called sublimation. The design is printed onto a roll of paper. This is wrapped around another roller which is both hot and heavy. The fabric is passed over this roller, and the dye is transferred to the fabric. It is a very fast process, and can be used for applying motifs as well as printing rolls of fabric.

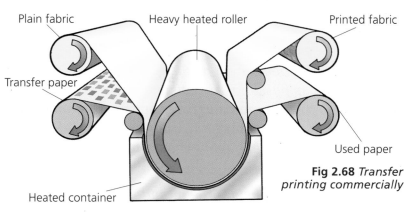

Fig 2.68 *Transfer printing commercially*

A simpler form of transfer printing can be used in school. Transfer inks are painted onto paper. This is then placed face down on the fabric and heat is applied to transfer the design onto the fabric. The design needs to be **inverted** before painting it onto the paper (Fig. 2.66). Designs created on a computer can be transferred onto fabric.

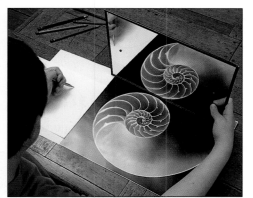

Fig. 2.69 *Transfer printing – using a mirror to invert the design*

Fig. 2.70 *Remember to protect your work area before spraying*

Other printing methods

There are a number of other ways of applying colour directly to fabric. The main ones are spraying and brushing.

Spraying fabrics with dye gives a subtle effect. It can be done using a toothbrush – this is dipped into dye then splattered onto the fabric; by using a diffuser and blowing the dye onto the fabric, or by using a compressed air spray gun. Whichever method is chosen, the fabric must be vertical, and any other objects nearby protected from the spray mist.

Brushing simply involves brushing dye directly onto the fabric. A range of brush sizes can be used to give different effects.

Dye pens and crayons are now available and provide a convenient way of creating a motif on a fabric. They are not suitable for longer pieces of fabric. They are used just like pens and crayons, and then the fabric is ironed to fix the dye.

Each of these techniques can be used alongside one of the other techniques described earlier. For example, fabric pens could be used to add detail to a screen printed image; fabric could be sprayed before it is printed using blocks; or fabric could be painted before it is screen printed.

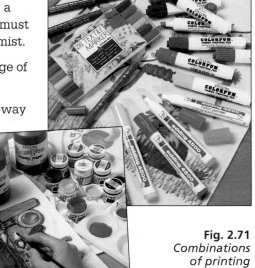

Fig. 2.71 *Combinations of printing techniques*

Making textile products

Textile products need to be made to the highest standards, whilst being as cost effective as possible. As consumers we expect our clothing and other textile items to look good and carry out their intended use. At all stages in the process of manufacturing textile products, designers and manufacturers build in quality checks to ensure that the product will serve its function.

Designers need to consider the intended use of the item when deciding the types of fibre to use, the method of manufacture and any trimmings that may be needed.

This chapter examines how to measure, mark, cut, shape, join and finish textile items that you could make in school.

Using patterns

Once a pattern has been developed, modelled and refined it needs to be cut from fabric. This is one of the most important stages in making any textile item, as mistakes made at this stage can be very costly. Before cutting out check:

■ that the pattern is the correct size;

■ the number of pieces that need to be cut from each pattern piece – draw a chart to show this;

■ if pieces need to be placed on the fabric in a particular direction;

■ how the fabric is to be folded – along its warp or along the weft? It is usual to fold the right sides of the fabric together. This keeps it clean and prevents the face of the material being damaged as pattern markings are transferred;

■ if the construction or design of the fabric means that the pattern pieces need to match. For example, it is important that pattern pieces cut from fabrics with a **nap** are all placed in the **same** direction. If not, the finished item will reflect light in different ways, making it appear that different coloured fabrics had been used. Extra fabric will be needed if striped, checked or a repeat design is used so that the pattern pieces can be matched.

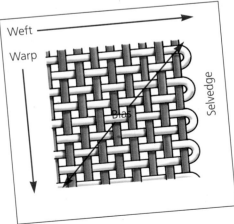

Fig. 3.1 *Warp, weft and bias*

Placing the pattern

A fabric's strength is along the warp. This needs to be taken into account when deciding which way to place pattern pieces on the fabric. As a rule, pattern pieces are placed with their grain line running parallel to the warp threads of the fabric. This is called the **straight grain**. Pattern pieces can sometimes be placed on the 'cross' (bias) of the fabric. This means that they are placed at a 45° angle to the warp threads. Placing pattern pieces on to the fabric on the bias enables the fabric to drape attractively and to be stretched whilst joining.

Shop bought pattern pieces have a double arrow which indicates the direction to place the pattern on to the fabric, so that the arrow is parallel to the straight grain. It is important to check this accurately, as the drape of an item can be affected. Fig. 3.2 shows how to do this using a tape measure or ruler. A pin should be placed at the top and bottom of the grain line to hold it in place.

Pinning fabric

When pinning pattern pieces into position on the fabric, take care that the edges of the pins do not go over the edge of the pattern. This will prevent you from cutting accurately. Place large pieces first, then fit smaller pieces in between, taking care not to waste fabric. This is very important in commercial manufacture as an extra few centimetres of unused fabric can be very expensive when several hundred items are being cut at once. The arrangement of pattern pieces on a length of fabric is called the **lay**. Commercially, this is done using computer design software.

Before cutting the fabric, check again that the pattern is pinned on correctly so that the correct number of pieces will be cut.

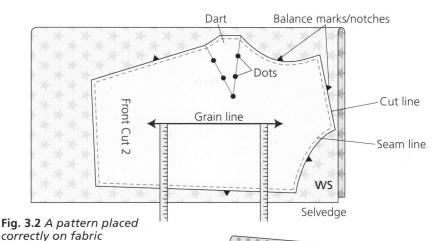

Fig. 3.2 *A pattern placed correctly on fabric*

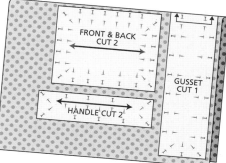

Fig. 3.3 *Pattern pieces for a bag pinned correctly on fabric*

Cutting fabric

It is important to use **dressmakers shears** for cutting fabric. These are very sharp and have long thin blades with handles designed to be comfortable to hold. These scissors should not be used for any other purpose as they will quickly become blunt. The long blades mean that straight, even cuts can be made in the fabric leaving smooth edges. Place one hand lightly on the pattern pinned to the fabric and cut around it, leave the fabric on the table top while cutting – do not pick it up as it could slip and the pattern will not be followed accurately.

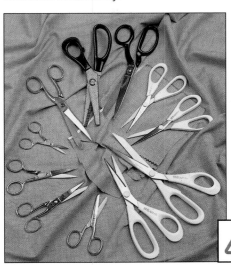

Fig. 3.5 *Types of scissors*

Clockwise from top: cutting-out shears, embroidery scissors, sewing scissors, dressmakers shears, all-purpose scissors, round-ended scissors, pointed scissors, embroidery scissors, smaller embroidery scissors, cutting out scissors and pinking shears.

 Handle scissors with care!

Fig. 3.4 *In industry many layers of fabric can be cut at once using a straight knife*

The fabric is cut following the outer edge of the pattern. Remember to cut around any balance marks or notches on the pattern.

It is likely that you will cut only two or three layers of fabric at school. In industry, many layers of fabric are cut at once using a straight knife, rather like a band saw, or by pressing using a die (a shaped cutter). This is quite expensive to set up so it is only used if many thousands of identical items are to be produced.

Marking

A lot of information about the way to construct a product is given on the pattern. This information is necessary during the manufacture of textile products to make sure that:

- all pattern pieces are joined together accurately;
- darts, tucks or pleats are made in the correct place;
- additional functional or decorative items such as pockets, fastenings or stitching are in the correct place.

Information about all of these important features can be found on shop-bought patterns. It is important that you include this information when you make your own patterns.

This information needs to be transferred to the fabric as accurately as possible, so that the product can be accurately constructed.

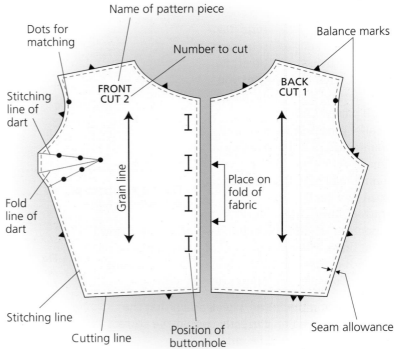

Fig. 3.6 *Pattern markings*

Transferring pattern marks

The main ways of transferring the pattern markings are:

- by using tailor's chalk;
- specifically designed pens;
- carbon paper;
- tailor's tacking.

None of these methods leave permanent marks. The method chosen will depend on the availability of equipment, the type of fabric used, how many pattern markings there are and how quickly the item is to be made up.

Tailor's chalk

This chalk is available in a range of colours, in either thin shaped slices or as a pencil. It does not leave permanent marks on fabric, and it can be easily rubbed off. Tailor's chalk works well on fairly smooth, non-stretchy fabrics.

1 Lift the pattern slightly away from the fabric.
2 Use a small cross, a line or a dot to transfer marks from the pattern to the fabric.
3 If two or more pieces have been cut, remove the pattern and place it on to the wrong side of the second piece of fabric. (You will need to turn the pattern piece over so that the printed side is against the fabric).
4 Again use a small mark to transfer marks from your pattern to the fabric.
5 Check that all of the markings for each pattern piece used have been marked on the fabric.

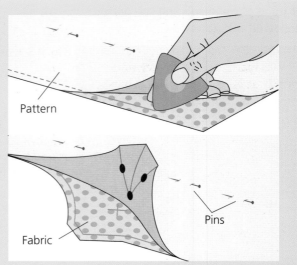

Fig. 3.7 *Using tailor's chalk*

Pens

It is possible to buy special felt-tip pens containing ink that can be washed out of fabric. They are very easy to use but only a limited range of colours is available. However, sometimes the ink will stain delicate fabrics. It is essential to test this out on a piece of spare fabric first. These pens tend to be more suitable for use on smooth, light coloured fabrics.

1 Lift the pattern slightly away from the fabric.
2 Place a mark such as a small cross, a line or a dot to transfer information from the pattern to the fabric.
3 If two or more pieces have been cut, remove the pattern and place it on to the wrong side of the another piece of fabric. (You will need to turn the pattern piece over so that the printed side is against the fabric).
4 Repeat step 2.
5 Transfer all the markings for each pattern piece used.
6 Once the product has been made, any visible pen marks can be removed using a damp cloth.

Carbon paper

Special dressmakers carbon paper, in a range of colours, can be bought this does not leave permanent marks on the fabric. A small wheel with spikes or grooves around its edge is used to transfer the pattern marking

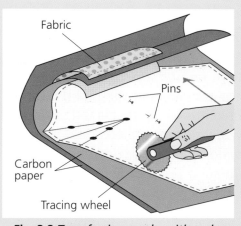

Fig. 3.8 *Transferring marks with carbon*

through the carbon paper on to the fabric. Carbon paper works well on fairly smooth, non-stretchy fabrics or light-coloured fabrics.

1 Lift the pattern off the fabric. Position one piece of carbon paper face down on top of the fabric and one face up against the bottom of the fabric.
   Note: If the fabric is thick, each layer of fabric may need to be marked separately.
2 Put the pattern back over the carbon. Press and run the wheel over the pattern mark to transfer essential information from the pattern to the fabric. Be careful not press too hard or the pattern could tear.
3 Transfer the markings for each pattern piece used.

Tailor's tacking

Tailor's tacking involves using a simple stitch which is easy to remove at a later stage. It can be used on any type or colour of fabric. Once the basic stitch has been learned, it is a quick and accurate way to transfer pattern markings.

1 Thread a needle with a long, double length of thread in a contrasting colour to the fabric.
2 Take a stitch through the pattern marking on to the fabric, leaving an end of about 2 cm.

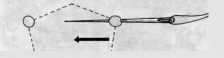

3 Take another stitch through the same point, leaving a loop of about 2 cm.
4 Cut the thread leaving an end of 2 cm.
5 Gently pull away the pattern piece leaving the tailors tack in the fabric.
6 Now ease the two layers of fabric apart and carefully cut the threads between the layers being careful not to cut the fabric.
7 Repeat marking for each pattern piece needed.

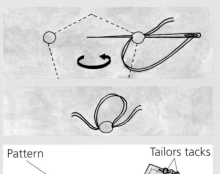

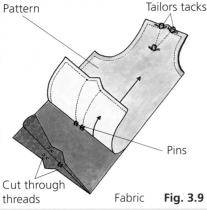

Fig. 3.9

Giving form to textile products

Most textile products are three-dimensional in form. Clothing is designed to fit around a person; seat covers fit around the shape of the seat; a tent fits the shape of the metal frame structure; a bag has space for belongings. However, all of these items are made from fabric which is two dimensional. Therefore techniques need to be used by both the designer and manufacturer in order that the finished product will meet its specification.

There are three ways of giving form to textile products:
- make the fabric three-dimensional as in warp knitting;
- use construction features such as darts, tucks and pleats to take away excess fabric from one place, but allow it in another;
- shape the pattern piece.

Very often these specific features are combined to produce the finished shape of textile products.

Shaping pattern pieces

A pattern piece may be shaped to give form to the textile product, and/or to add an interesting style detail.

Look at the photos of jeans in Fig. 3.10. One has been made from a pattern piece with straight edges, the other from a pattern piece which is shaped to provide more width at the bottom. This simple change makes a dramatic difference to the overall appearance of the jeans. There are many other textile products which rely on shaping pattern pieces to give form (e.g. parachutes, car seats and chair covers).

Fig. 3.10

Construction features

All construction features rely on the technique of taking excess fabric from one place whilst allowing it in another. The one chosen depends upon the type of product, the position of the feature, the design intention, and the final effect to be achieved.

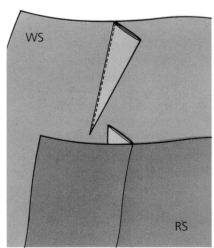

Fig. 3.11 *Darts*

Darts

Darts are a very effective way of providing a smooth solution to removing excess fullness. It is a technique frequently used on fitted clothing such as waistcoats, shirts, trousers, skirts, and household items such as furnishings. The effect on the outside of the product is a line, but a look inside will show that at one end is a large fold of fabric, which tapers to nothing at the other end. Sometimes darts are made to taper from the middle to either end.

Making a dart

1 Using the pattern markings to help matching, fold the fabric right sides (RS) together so that the dots match.
2 Pin and tack the dart along the stitching line.

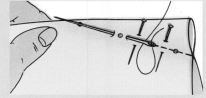

3 Starting at the outer edge, sew to a point at the end. It is important to taper the sewing line close to the fold.

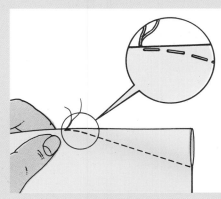

4 Secure the ends of thread.
5 Press horizontal darts downwards, and vertical darts away from the centre.
6 If the fabric is quite thick, it will be necessary to cut along the fold of the dart to within 10 mm of the point. This should then be pressed open, leaving a less bulky finish.

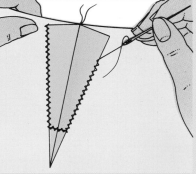

7 If the dart has two points, snip the middle of the dart towards the fold. This is necessary so that the dart will lie flat.

Fig. 3.12 *Stages in making a dart*

Gathers

This process involves gathering a wide piece of fabric to make it fit into a narrower piece. This effect can be used on a wide range of products such as curtains, bags, skirts and jackets. It is important that the fabric used is not too thick or stiff, as it will not gather easily, it will look very bulky, and will not drape well.

Fig. 3.13 *Gathers are used in many textile products*

Making gathers

1 Set the sewing machine to its longest stitch, and loosen the upper tension slightly. (This will allow you to easily pull the threads to form the gathers.)
2 Sew a line of stitching just inside the seam allowance, and another parallel line 5 mm away from this one. Leave the ends of the thread loose.

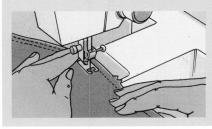

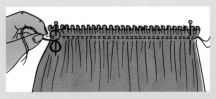

3 Place a pin vertically into the fabric at one end of the gathering threads.
4 Wrap the threads in a figure of 8 around the pin to stop the threads pulling through.
5 At the opposite end, carefully pull the top threads, easing the fabric along as you pull to form the gathers.
6 Keep pulling the threads until the fabric is reduced to the correct length.

7 Place another pin vertically into the fabric at this end of the gathering threads.
8 Wrap the top threads in a figure of 8 around the pin to hold the threads in position.
9 Now carefully ease the fabric along the gathers to spread the gathers evenly.
10 Make sure the gathers are lying flat.
11 The gathered fabric is now ready for joining to a flat piece of fabric.

Fig. 3.14 *Stages in making gathers*

Easing

Easing is useful when one piece of fabric is slightly larger than the piece it is being joined to. The technique is most often used when joining two curved pieces of fabric, as in a sleeve. Sometimes a single row of gathering can be used 10 mm from the outer edge of the outwards curve in order to make this process easier.

1 Place the two pieces of fabric right sides together, with the outwards curve facing you.
2 Place pin through the fabric to match any dots from the pattern.
3 Now place pins vertically at small, regular intervals along the length of the curve, gently easing in the excess fabric.
4 Tack carefully and remove pins before machine stitching.

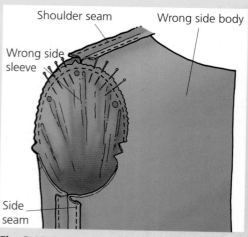

Fig. 3.15 *Easing used on a sleeve*

Tucks and pleats

Tucks are folds in fabric which are stitched to hold them in place. Pleats are also folds in fabric, but they are left unstitched. Both tucks and pleats are effective methods of reducing fullness, as well as being interesting design features.

Folding the fabric in different ways produces a wide range of interesting effects as can be seen in Fig. 3.16.

The process of making tucks and pleats is very similar.

1 Fold the fabric carefully following the pattern markings.
2 Be careful that the folds are in the correct direction and that the crease follows the straight grain of the fabric. This is very important or the pleat will not hang correctly.
3 Pin and tack down the length of the fold to hold it in place.

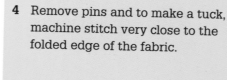

4 Remove pins and to make a tuck, machine stitch very close to the folded edge of the fabric.

5 Press pleats in place before joining to another piece of fabric.

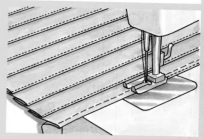

Fig. 3.16 *Pleats and tucks have many uses*

Fig. 3.17

Smocking

Smocking is a traditional way of decoratively reducing fullness. It uses many rows of gathering to pull the fabric into tight folds. These folds are then held in place with decorative hand embroidery or machine stitching. Combinations of stitches and colours can be used to create interesting effects. Traditionally white thread was used on white fabric to provide a subtle decoration. Often the occupation of the wearer was shown by the embroidery used!

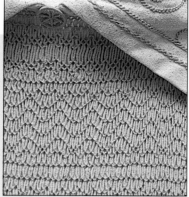
Fig. 3.18
Smocked top

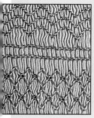

If smocking is to be used on clothing, the fabric used must be soft and fairly lightweight so that a soft, gathered effect is achieved. However, smocking can also be used on furnishing fabrics such as velvet and velour, for seat covers, cushions and other soft furnishings.

Fig. 3.19 *Traditional stitches*

1 Following information from the pattern, sew lines of parallel gathering threads.

2 Secure the threads at one end by wrapping the threads around a pin in a figure of 8.

3 Pull the top thread at the other end and adjust the gathers until they are evenly spaced and the fabric is the correct size to fit the piece of fabric it will be joined to.

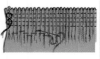

4 Secure the threads at this end by wrapping the threads around the pin in a figure of 8.

5 Using the lines of gathering threads as a guide, add the decorative stitching. Fig 3.19 shows some of the stitches traditionally used.

Stem stitch
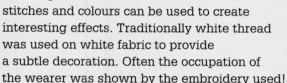
Cable stitch

Chevron stitch

Trellis stitch

Honeycomb stitch

Fig. 3.20 *Smocking stitches*

Gussets

These are extra pieces of fabric inserted between two flat pieces which give a three dimensional shape. Gussets are often used in furnishings, in bags and cushions.

Fig. 3.21 *Items with a gusset*

Making a gusset

1 Measure around the edges of the fabric where the gusset is to be joined.

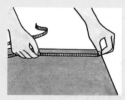

2 Decide on the width of the gusset, add a seam allowance of 15 mm to both edges.

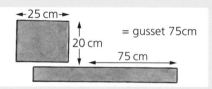
25 cm · 20 cm · = gusset 75 cm · 75 cm

3 Cut out fabric to the correct size. You might need to cut out two pieces and join them along the shortest edge.

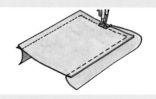

4 With the right sides of the fabric together, pin, tack and sew the gusset along one edge.

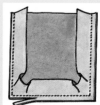

5 Repeat along the other side.

6 Press and trim corners and seam allowance (see page 68).

Fig. 3.22

Joining fabric pieces

The individual parts of textile products are joined temporarily using pins and tacking stitches before being more permanently joined using machine stitching. Temporary joining has two main functions – to check that pattern pieces match together correctly and to hold pieces together firmly before stitching.

Seams and **fastenings** are used in order to join the fabric pieces together. Seams provide a more permanent solution while fastenings enable openings to be created which allow the item to be easily removed. The method of joining needs to be carefully considered. It is important to think about:

- how strong the join needs to be;
- if the join is to have a decorative as well as a functional use;
- how durable the join needs to be;
- if the position of the join affects how comfortable the product is to use or wear;
- how much time the join will take to construct.

Equipment used for joining

Hand tools

Dressmakers pins, needles and sewing thread are all needed for temporary joining.

Pins should be sharp and free from rust. Place pins at right angles to the edge of the fabric with the points of the pins facing inwards. This will hold the fabric pieces together securely and prevent the pins from pricking your fingers as you work.

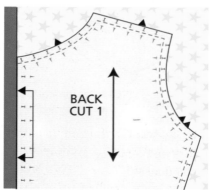

Fig. 3.23 *Pins placed correctly*

Different types of **sewing needles** are produced for different purposes. The type of thread, the thickness of the fabric and the type of sewing affect the choice of needle to be used. The needle needs to be thick enough to make a hole for the thread to pass through the fabric, without damaging it by leaving a large hole. This means that thin needles should be used on fine fabrics. Fig. 3.24 shows the types of needles used for specific purposes.

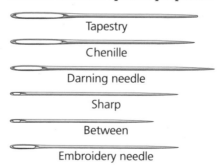

Tapestry

Chenille

Darning needle

Sharp

Between

Embroidery needle

Fig. 3.24

Soft unfinished thread can be used for tacking. This can be bought fairly cheaply on large reels and as it is soft, it is easy to take out later. Most sewing thread is made from polyester or is a mixture of polyester and cotton. It is tightly twisted into a range of different thicknesses.

Machine tools

Sewing machines

Sewing machines and **overlockers** are used for permanent joining. Sewing machines make a lock stitch using two threads – one on a reel at the top and one on a spool at the bottom. As the machine needle moves down, the spool at the bottom rotates. A hook on the spool case forms a loop around the top thread and teeth on the feed move the fabric forward. It is important that the tension of the top and bottom threads allows this loop to sit in between the layers of the fabric. If the top tension is too tight, the loop will sit on the top surface of the fabric and the material will be pulled. If the top tension is too loose, the loop will sit on the bottom surface of the fabric. A loose top tension is, however, useful when **gathering** as the threads can be easily pulled.

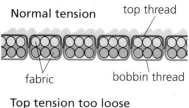

Normal tension

top thread

fabric

bobbin thread

Top tension too loose

Top tension too tight

Fig. 3.25 *Normal, tight and loose, top tension*

Fig. 3.26 *Threading a spool*

Thread winding in clockwise direction

Tension slit

Tension spring

'Click'

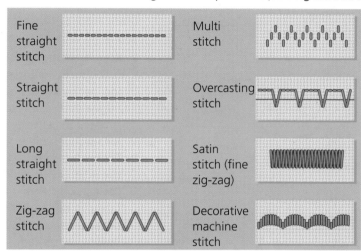

Thread guide

Take up lever

LCD display

Spool pin (for cotton reel)

Balance wheel

Frame for decorative stitching

Bobbin case

Presser foot

Fig. 3.27 *Computerised sewing machine*

The length and width of stitches can be adjusted on sewing machines. Many machines contain microprocessors which enable them to be programmed to sew a range of plain and decorative stitches. Some machines can be linked directly to a computer, enabling designs to be embroidered directly on to fabric.

As with hand sewing it is important to choose the correct type and size of needle according to the thickness of fabric being sewn. If knitted or stretchy fabrics are being sewn a ball point needle is used. This has a rounded end which pushes the fibres apart and prevents the fabric laddering. Twin needles can be used to sew two parallel lines of stitching. This decorative effect looks like lines of pintucks when sewn on fine fabrics.

Overlockers

Overlockers can stitch and finish the edges of seams in one operation. As the machine sews it makes a straight stitch along the seam line and cuts the seam allowance back. At the same time, the overlocker sews looped stitches along the edge of the fabric to prevent it from fraying. Overlockers are also very useful for sewing knitted fabrics as this type of stitching can stretch along with the fabric and does not break.

Other equipment needed

The most important items of equipment apart from a sewing machine are the **iron** and ironing board. As fabrics are joined, seams need to be pressed open so that they lie flat. If this is not done the finished product will not hang well and small tucks may be seen at joins. A steam iron is best, but if one is not available then use a damp cloth over the fabric.

Fine straight stitch		Multi stitch	
Straight stitch		Overcasting stitch	
Long straight stitch		Satin stitch (fine zig-zag)	
Zig-zag stitch		Decorative machine stitch	

Fig. 3.28 *Different machine stitches*

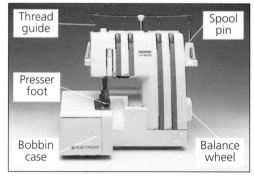

Thread guide

Spool pin

Presser foot

Bobbin case

Balance wheel

Fig. 3.29 *An overlocker*

Fig. 3.30 *Other equipment needed when joining fabrics*

Use the point of the iron to open seams and to get into corners. Always press on the wrong side of the fabric so that you do not leave heat marks on the right side.

Other smaller pieces of equipment needed include a tape measure, tailor's chalk, dressmaking scissors and small sharp scissors.

Seams

A seam is a join between two pieces of fabric. A wide range of seams can be used depending on the fabric, the item being made and if the join is to be decorative. The finished seam should be smooth, hold the product together and give shape and emphasis.

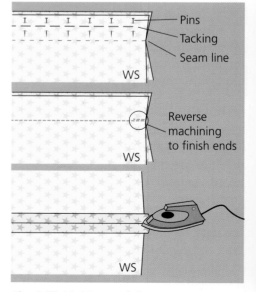

Fig. 3.31

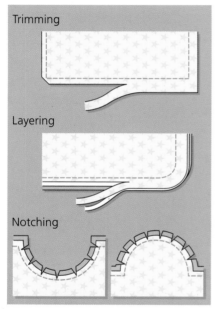

Fig. 3.32 *Neatening seams*

Before beginning construction there are four techniques which you need to be familiar with.

1 **Staystitching** is a line of machine stitching sewn 3 mm inside the seam line on curved edges and on stretchy fabrics. It helps to prevent the fabric loosing its shape.
2 **Trimming** refers to reducing the seam allowance after sewing on items where the fabric is bulky. Allowances are usually trimmed to 6 mm before neatening.
3 **Layering (Grading)** is used when there are two or more layers of fabric turn together in one direction. It helps to reduce bulk enabling the seam to lie flat. Each layer is trimmed to a different width. The most important piece is left with the widest seam allowance.
4 **Clipping (notching;snipping)** are usually used to help curved seams to lie flat. If the seams need layering or trimming this is done first. On inward curves, snip the seam allowance at right angles to the seam at regular intervals – every 5–10 mm; on outward curves cut out a small triangle (notch) of fabric. Be careful not to clip the machine stitching.

Plain seam

This is the most widely used seam. It is very quick to construct, it is not bulky and can be used on a wide range of fabrics.

Making a plain seam

1 Place the fabric pieces right sides together.
2 Match any balance marks or dots, then pin in place.
3 Tack just inside the seam allowance. Begin the tacking with a knot and secure the ends with a double stitch. Remove the pins.
4 Sew along the seam line, starting and finishing with reverse machine stitching to secure the threads. Stitch a second line just inside the seam allowance on any areas that are likely to be exposed to stress. If the fabric is stretchy, choose a wide zig-zag stitch or stretch stich as this will stretch along with the fabric.
5 Remove the tacking stitches.
6 Press the seam open on the wrong side.

Fig. 3.33 *Making a plain seam*

Finishing a plain seam

It is important to finish the inside edges of a plain seam to prevent the fabric from fraying during use or laundering. There are a range of different possibilities depending of the fabric, the location of the seam and the use of the product.

Fig. 3.34 shows some of the finishes that can be used.

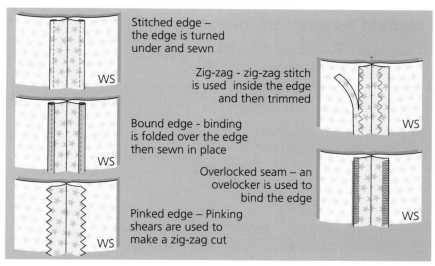

Stitched edge – the edge is turned under and sewn

Zig-zag - zig-zag stitch is used inside the edge and then trimmed

Bound edge - binding is folded over the edge then sewn in place

Overlocked seam – an ovelocker is used to bind the edge

Pinked edge – Pinking shears are used to make a zig-zag cut

Fig. 3.34

Overlaid (lapped) seam

This a very quick seam to make. It is often used over gathered, pleated or tucked areas of a product, but can also be used on flat fabric. Extra trimmings such as lace, braid, covered piping or contrasting pieces of fabric can be sandwiched between the layers to add decorative interest. Fig. 3.36 shows the stages in making an overlaid seam.

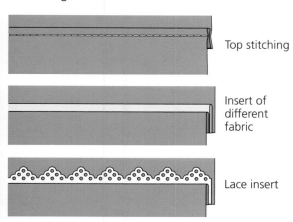

Top stitching

Insert of different fabric

Lace insert

Fig. 3.35 *A decorative overlaid seam*

French seam

This is a very strong smooth seam which does not show on the right side of the product, but its construction means that it can only be used on fine fabrics. It is frequently used on underclothes and nightwear. It is a little harder to make than plain or lapped seams.
You can see how to make one on the next page (Fig. 3.37).

Making an overlaid seam

1 Take the top piece of fabric and press its seam allowance to the wrong side.

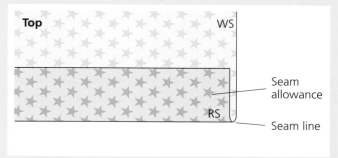

Seam allowance

Seam line

2 Lay this folded edge over the seam line of the other piece and pin in place.
3 Make sure that the seam edge is correctly positioned, then tack.
4 Sew close to the folded edge of the upper fabric and press the seam.

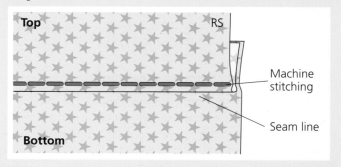

Machine stitching

Seam line

5 Layer the seam allowance on the wrong side so that it lies flat.
6 The raw edges can be finished using a zig-zag machine stitch, by binding the edge, or by using pinking shears.

Fig. 3.36

Making a French seam

1. Place the fabric wrong sides together, match balance marks and dots. Pin in place.
2. Tack close to the edge and remove pins.
3. Sew the pieces together 5 mm from the seam line.

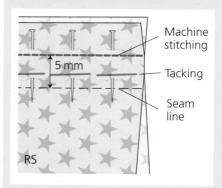

Fig. 3.37

4. Remove the tacking. Trim the seam to less than 3 mm from the stitching.

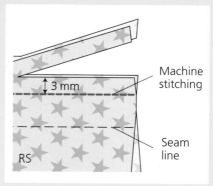

5. Press the seam open.
6. Turn the fabric so that the right sides are together. Roll the line of the seam between your fingers so that the seam line is on the top edge. Pin in place.

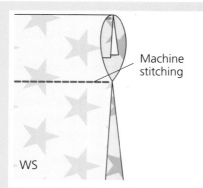

7. Measure, pin and tack 5 mm from the seam line and remove pins.
8. Sew 10 mm from the edge being careful not to pull the fabric.
9. Remove the tacking.
10. Press the seam towards the back or downwards according to its location on the product.

Double-stitched (run and fell) seam

This is a very strong seam, but it is quite bulky. It is used on areas of heavy wear and for decorative reasons such as the outer leg seam in jeans. Fig. 3.38 shows you how to make one.

Making a double stitched seam

1. Place the wrong sides of the fabric together and match any balance marks or dots.
2. Pin in place. Tack 10 mm from the edge and remove pins.

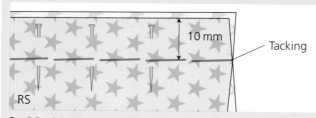

3. Machine stitch 15 mm from the edge.

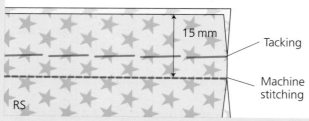

4. Remove the tacking and press the seam towards the back.

5. Trim the underneath layer to 3 mm and the upper layer to 10 mm.

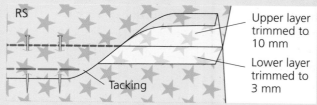

6. Fold in the edge of the upper layer, then lay over under layer to enclose it. Pin and tack in place.
7. Take out pins and machine stitch close to the folded edge.

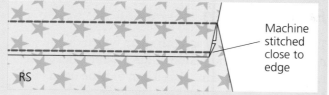

8. Remove tacking and press seam with iron.
Note: If the right sides of the fabric are placed together in step 1 only one line of stitching will be visible on the finished product.

Fig. 3.38

Fastenings

Fastenings allow textile items to be put on or taken off easily, to be removed for cleaning, or to secure something which needs to be opened easily (like a bag). The fastening holds the item together while it is in use.

A wide range of fastenings are available which can be both decorative and functional. The fastening chosen depends on the function of the item, the fabric used and if it is to be seen. For example, a costume to be used in the theatre will need a fastening which is quick to undo. A child's coat needs a fastening which is easy to handle and can be done up quickly.

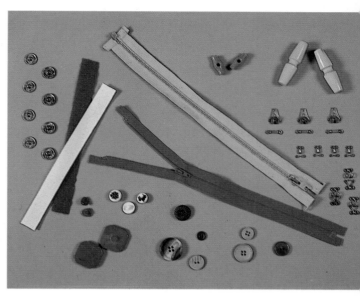

Fig. 3.39 *A range of fastenings*

Velcro

This is the newest type of fastening available and is extremely versatile. Velcro consists of two pieces of polyamide tape. One piece has a covering of fine loops and the other a covering of fine hooks. When these are pressed together they join and give a strong fastening. With a little effort they can be pulled apart. Velcro has a wide range of uses including fastenings for shoes, outdoor clothing, furnishings, car seat covers and tent flaps.

Velcro is bought in strips. These are either sewn by hand or machine down each edge or can be glued on to the fabric.

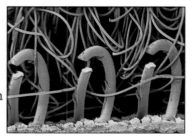

Fig. 3.40 *Velcro as seen under a microscope*

Eyelets

Eyelets are holes in fabric through which a lace or cord can be threaded. Eyelets can be made and sewn by hand, but usually an eyelet tool is used to press a metal ring around the hole.

Zips

Zips are a strong, quick and versatile fastening which can be concealed or visible to provide interesting style detail. Zips consist of two tapes with teeth along one edge. As the slider is pulled these join together providing a secure fastening. A wide range of colours, weights and sizes can be bought to suit almost any purpose. These include:

■ open–ended zips for fastening jackets and coats;
■ invisible zips where the zip teeth are on the inside of the product;
■ curved zips for use in trousers.

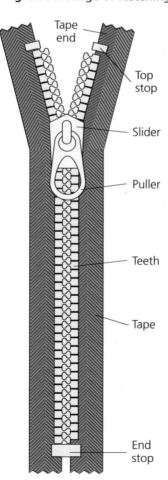

Fig. 3.41 *Parts of a zip*

Inserting a zip

There are several different ways of putting in a zip. A special presser foot can be used on most machines for sewing zips. This allows the needle to sew very close to one edge of the foot so that it is possible to sew near to the teeth of the zip.

Edge to edge

This is the most common way of inserting a zip. It provides a symmetrical finish and as it is not bulky it can be used on heavy weight fabrics.

1 Sew the seam up to the place where you want to insert the zip. The top of the zip teeth should be just below the seam line.

2 Change the machine stitch to sew a long stitch and continue to sew the seam (you could also do this with tacking). This will hold the two sides of the seam together while you insert the zip.

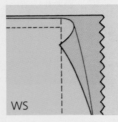

3 Press the seam open along its length.

4 Place the zip right side down on to the wrong side of the seam. Position the zip so that the slider is 25 mm from the top of the seam. Make sure that the teeth are positioned over the centre line of the seam.

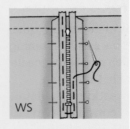

5 Beginning at the top, pin the zip in place and then tack using the lines in the zip tape as a guide.

6 Remove the pins and turn the fabric over. Sew down the first side of the zip following the tacking line. When you reach the end of the first side, leave the needle in the fabric, raise the foot and pivot the fabric. Lower the foot to sew across the bottom of the zip.

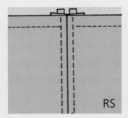

7 Count the number of stitches needed to reach the seam line, then sew this number on the other side, so that the two lines of stitching are the same distance from the centre.

8 Pivot again and then sew up the other side.

9 Press and remove all tacking.

10 Neaten the edges of the seam.

Fig. 3.42

Concealed zip

This is another popular method of inserting a zip, which covers the zip completely. It is often used on light and medium weight fabrics.

1 Sew the seam up to the place where you want to insert the zip. The top of the zip teeth should be just below the seam line. Press the seam open and neaten the edges.

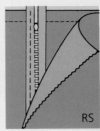

2 Place the zip face down on the underside opening of the seam, so that the zip teeth are 2 mm over the seam line. Pin and tack in place.

3 Sew down this edge, close to the zip teeth. The best results are obtained by using a special zip foot for this.

4 Press the zip back, so that the right side of the zip is facing you.

5 Lay the upper part of the seam opening over the zip, keeping the seam lines together.

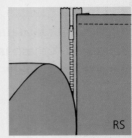

6 Tack, then sew from the top down to about 3 mm past the stop at the end of the zip.

7 Pivot the fabric, then sew towards the seam line, either with a straight line of stitching, or at an angle.

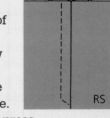

8 Remove the tacking then press.

Fig. 3.43

Buttons

Buttons are used with button holes, loops made from thread or fabric to hold edges of fabric together. A wide range of colours, sizes and styles can be bought. Buttons are made from a range of materials including polyester, metal and wood. It is also possible to buy buttons which can be covered with fabric to match the product being made. Choose buttons which will withstand wear and be resistant to washing and dry cleaning.

Also, as they are usually conspicuous, care needs to be taken to choose both the buttons and the way of fastening them which will best fit your product.

Buttons which have a loop or extension underneath are called shanks. The shank raises the button from the surface of the fabric. If a flat button is used, a shank needs to be sewn, otherwise the button will be difficult to fasten.

Making buttonholes

The position of buttonholes is usually shown on a pattern. If the pattern has been altered, the position of the buttonhole may also need to be altered. The buttonhole is made before sewing on a button. It needs to be large enough for the button to pass through, but not so large that the button will unfasten when worn. Buttonholes can be positioned either vertically or horizontally. Vertical buttonholes are used when there is little strain on the fastening. For example down the front of a shirt. Horizontal buttonholes are used when there is more strain on the button. For example on the collar of a shirt, or the waistband of trousers.

There are various ways of making buttonholes according to the type of product, the fabric and its position. Machined buttonholes are the most versatile and quick to make. Many machines can be programmed to sew buttonholes automatically (see Fig. 3.44).

Press studs

These are used on overlapping openings where there is not much strain. They are easy to use and quick to apply. Press studs have two parts – one has a small ball in the centre, the other a small cup which holds the ball in place when the two parts are pressed together. They can be made from polyester or metal, bought in a range of sizes and with decorative covers on the outside. The part with the ball is sewn on to the under side of the top layer of the fabric, while the socket is sewn on to the top side of the bottom layer. Sew studs on securely, making sure that each part lines up correctly.

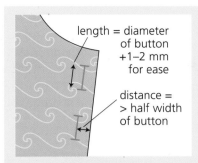

length = diameter of button +1–2 mm for ease

distance = > half width of button

1   Mark the position of the buttonhole carefully. Check that it is long enough for the button to fit through. Make sure it is more than half the width of the button from the edge of the fabric. This will ensure that the button does not overlap the edge of the fabric when fastened.

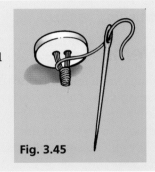

2   Place a buttonhole foot in the sewing machine. Programme the machine and sew the buttonhole.
3   Secure loose ends.
4   Cut down the middle of the buttonhole with sharp, pointed scissors, being careful not to cut the threads.   Fig. 3.44

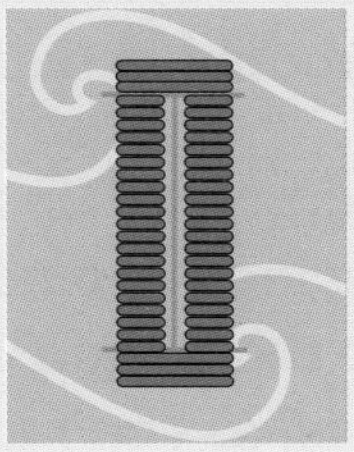

Sewing on buttons

1   Place the button in the correct position.
2   Sew through the holes in the button. Hold the button in place carefully as you sew.
3   If necessary make a shank. This simply involves wrapping the thread several times around the sewing threads between the button and fabric.
4   Secure the end firmly.

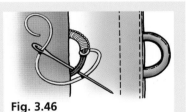

Fig. 3.45

Making loops

There are two ways of making loops for use with buttons - using thread or by using fabric loops called rouleau loops. Fig 3.46 shows the result of these two types of loop.

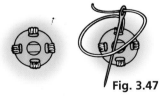

Fig. 3.46

Fig. 3.47

Hooks and eyes or bars

These are used on areas where there is a lot of strain, such as waistbands. The hook is placed on the under side of the upper part of the opening. This ensures that the edge of the hook is level with the edge of the opening. The bar or eye is placed on the lower part of the opening. Sew securely and stitch to hold the loop of the hook flat against the fabric.

Fig. 3.48

Finishing edges

It is important that all raw edges of fabric have a suitable finish applied to them. As products are used or cleaned, unfinished edges will fray. This will reduce the life of the product and also look unattractive.

Edges can be finished using hems, facings or bindings. These often add to the design detail of the product as well as their intended functional purpose. (See p.69 for information on finishing seams.)

Hems

Hems are a fold of fabric turned to the wrong side. They provide a versatile way of finishing a raw edge. Sometimes they add weight to a product and improve its drape. They can be sewn by hand or machine and the stitching can be invisible or visible and decorative. Some hems can be glued together using bondaweb. Edgings such as braid, lace and tassels can add decorative interest. Some hems can be made to hold tape or elastic – these are called **casings**. Various types of hem are shown in Fig.3.49

It is important to make sure that the edge of the hem is level and that it is of even width. Any visible stitching must be even and straight. Any raw edges on the wrong side need to be finished (Fig.3.50).

The construction of hems

1 A small hem should be used on fine fabrics. The edge of the fabric should be turned over twice and then either hand sewn or machine stitched to hold it in place.

2 A stronger hem is needed on medium weight fabric. Zig-zag the edge of your fabric then fold over and use a herringbone stitch. This could also be machined using a blind hemmer.

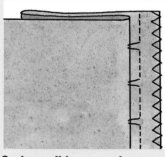

3 A small hem can be finished with a double line of stitching to form a casing.

4 Hem with tassels attached.

5 Hem with braid applied.

6 Using a hot iron with bondaweb.

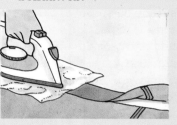

7 Decorative shell edging using sewing machine.

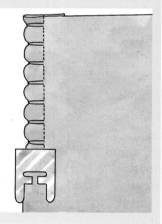

Fig. 3.49

Finishes for raw edges of hems

1 On light fabrics edges should be turned and machine stitched.

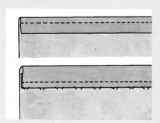

2 Zig-zag edges should be used on fabrics of a medium or heavy weight.

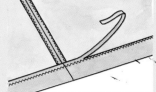

3 Attaching binding on medium or heavy weight fabrics.

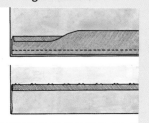

4 Making small tucks to deal with excess fullness in hems.

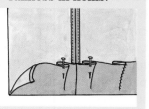

Fig. 3.50

Facings

Facings are pieces of fabric used to finish raw edges. They give stability and emphasise the shape. Facings are usually invisible on the right side of the fabric, but occasionally they can be used as a design feature. Facings are the same shape as the edge which is to be covered. Interfacing is usually applied to the wrong side of the facing in order to give extra stability. The weight of interfacing used should be similar to the weight of the fabric. Figs. 3.51 and 3.52 show examples of attaching facings.

How to apply a straight facing to the top edge of a bag

1 Machine stitch or iron interfacing to the wrong side of your facing.

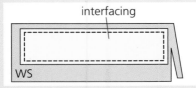
interfacing
WS

2 Trim interfacing close to the stitching.
3 Turn one long edge of facing over on to the wrong side by 5 mm and machine stitch close to the edge.

WS

4 Place the right sides of the facing to the right sides of the bag. Carefully match up the edges.

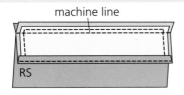
machine line
RS

5 Pin, tack and then machine stitch 15 mm from the edge.

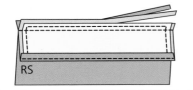
RS

6 Trim and layer the edges.
7 Press the seam towards the facing.

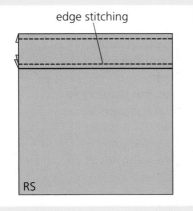
edge stitching
RS

8 Open the facing and then stitch close to the edge of the bag.   **Fig. 3.51**

Adding curved facings to a neckline

a

WS
RS

1 Pin, tack then sew the facing at the shoulder seams, trim and press open.
2 Apply interfacing.
3 Neaten the outside edge of your facing - use a zig-zag stitch on stretchy fabrics.
4 Put the right sides of your fabric together and pin the facing to the neckline of the vest then tack it into place.
5 Machine stitch the facing to the neckline.

6 Clip the seam allowance at 4 or 5 cm intervals then layer the edge turnings to reduce bulk.

b
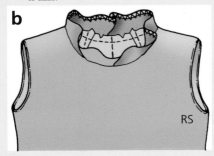
RS

7 Press the facing with the seam towards the facing.
8 Stitch the facing close to the edge of the seam catching in the turnings. This helps the facing to lie flat.

c
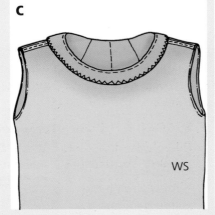
WS

9 Press the facing to the wrong side of the vest.
10 Stitch the edge of the facing to the shoulder seam of the vest to hold the facing in place.

Fig 3.52

Bindings

Bindings are used to finish and give stability to raw edges. Unlike facings, a binding can be seen on both the right side and the wrong side of the product. The binding often adds design detail to the product as contrasting colours or different fabrics can be used.

Placing binding on straight and curved edges

1 Place the right side of the binding to the right side of the fabric.
2 Pin, tack and then machine stitch along the folded edge.

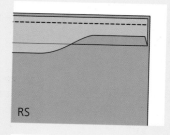

3 Iron the binding so that it stands up.
4 Roll the binding over the edge.
5 Use a slip stitch on the wrong side of the fabric to secure the fabric.

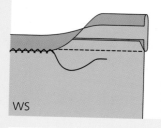

6 Check that the finished binding looks the same on both sides.

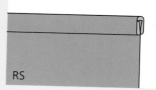

7 On inwards curves ease the binding around the curve. Finish as for straight edges.

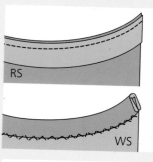

8 On outwards curves stretch the binding around the curve. Finish as for straight edges.

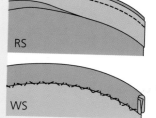

Fig. 3.54

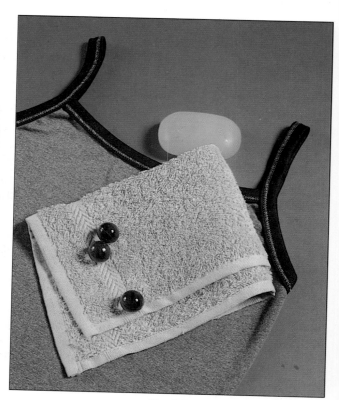

Fig. 3.53 *Binding has been used on this top and facecloth*

Bindings can be used on both straight and curved edges. Binding used on curved edges must be capable of stretching. This is called **bias binding**. Bias binding can be bought ready made or bias strips can be cut from fabric.

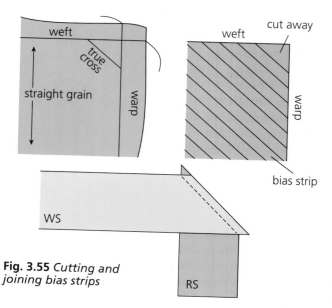

Fig. 3.55 *Cutting and joining bias strips*

Piping

Piping is a folded piece of fabric trapped between two layers of fabric. It can be used together with a facing or binding to add design detail or as part of a seam. The piping can have cord inserted into it which makes the edge stand out. Figs. 3.57 and 3.58 show the stages of inserting piping.

Fig. 3.56 *Cord piping makes edges stand out*

Inserting piping

1 Cut a piece of fabric that is twice the width that you want your finished piping to be plus an allocation for seams.
2 Fold the cut fabric in half with the wrong sides together.

3 Pin and tack the piping fabric on to the right side of one piece of your main fabric.
4 Place the other piece of fabric on top, sandwiching the piping between the two main layers of fabric.

6 Press the piping on to the right side of the fabric.
7 Machine stitch (through all the layers) close to the seam.
8 Trim and layer the seam allowance.

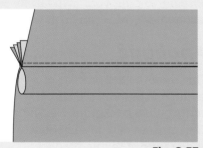

5 Pin and tack. Remove the pins and machine stitch through all the layers of fabric.

Fig. 3.57

Inserting cord piping

1 Fold your chosen piping in half wrong sides together, but <u>do not</u> press.
2 Place the cord inside the piping and then pin and tack close to the cord.

4 Sandwich the piping between the two main layers of your fabric, with the right sides together.

5 Again pin and tack the layers of fabric close to the cord. Remove the pins and machine stitch using a zip foot.
6 Trim and layer the seam.

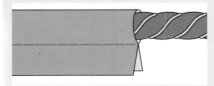

3 Machine stitch as close to the cord as you can. This will be easier if you use a zip foot on your machine.

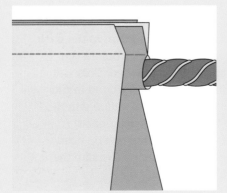

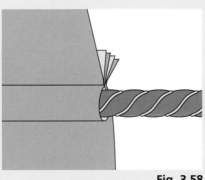

Fig. 3.58

Customising and personalising textiles

Many textile products are mass produced. This term refers to the manufacturing processes which enable large numbers of identical products to be made. While this enables the products to be bought more cheaply, not everyone wants to be seen in the same clothing as everyone else! **Haute couture** clothing is at the opposite end of the scale. These items are individually designed and produced. As a result they are very expensive, but they are unique.

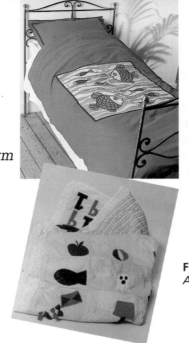

Fig. 3.59
Appliquéd textiles

There are some simple techniques which can be used to customise textile products you make. In chapter 2, there is information about printing and dyeing your own fabrics. This is an excellent starting point for creating customised products. However, it is not always possible to print your own fabric. There are a range of other techniques which can be used to customise your products.

Appliqué

This refers to the process of laying one or more pieces of fabric onto a background fabric. This process can be seen on a wide range of textile products. It is used to:

- emphasise a design feature;
- add colour;
- to decorate a product.

Designs can be big and bold using only few pieces of fabric or they can be more intricate using layers of fabrics. This would require more skill and care when sewing. Further stitching can be added on top of the appliqué to add detail. Ribbon, tape and braid can also be applied to fabrics.

Choice of fabrics

A wide range of fabrics can be used, but it is a good idea to choose fabrics with similar care requirements as the product you are decorating. A cotton product with a silk appliqué design will have to be cared for as silk, as the higher temperatures that cotton can withstand would damage the silk.

Fabrics which fray badly should have **interfacing** ironed on to the wrong side of the fabric before the individual pieces are cut out. This helps to prevent the edges fraying and makes the appliqué firmer, providing a more professional finish. Interfacing can also be ironed on to the back of stretchy fabrics before the appliqué is attached. This will prevent the background fabric stretching out of shape where the appliqué is positioned. A layer of wadding can be used under each shape to make the appliqué stand out.

1 Draw the design to scale on paper.

2 Iron interfacing on to fabrics which fray.

3 Cut out the individual pieces making sure that the warp on each piece matches the warp of the background fabric. This will prevent the appliqué from puckering after washing.

4 Pin and tack each piece in place. The edges of fine fabrics can be turned in before stitching in place. If there are several layers of appliqué begin with the pieces at the bottom and work upwards.

5 Apply to the background fabric following one of the methods on page 79.

Fig. 3.60

Fixing appliqué to a background

Hand sewing

This is a time consuming task! Stitching must be very neat and needs to fasten each piece securely to the background. Herringbone stitch can be used on fabrics which fray or slip stitching used on fabrics with a turned in edge.

Fig. 3.61 *Pieces applied using herringbone stitch*

Machine sewing

Zig-zag (satin stitch) stitching can be used for pieces which fray and edge stitching is used on pieces with turned edges.

Zig-zag

1 Set a wide stitch width and short length. Use an embroidery foot on the machine as this will allow the stitching to pass easily through. The thread can match or contrast with the appliqué. Contrasting stitching must be sewn very accurately or the appearance of the finished product will be spoiled.

2 Position the needle so that the right hand edge of the stitch is still on the piece to be attached. Carefully stitch all around the piece ensuring that threads are secured at the start and finish.

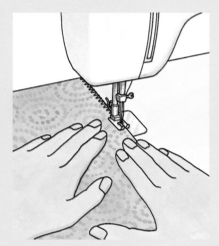

3 Using sharp pointed scissors trim away any excess fabric close to the stitching, being careful not to cut the stitching or background fabric. This is easier to do if you roll the stitched edge of the appliqué over your forefinger.

4 Continue stitching each piece in the same way.

5 Press the appliqué.

Turning corners

1 Machine down one side, finishing with the needle on the outer edge.

2 Make sure the needle is in the fabric.

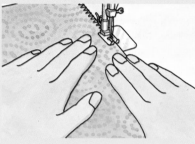

3 Raise the presser foot. Rotate the fabric so the next outer edge to be sewn is on the right.

4 Lower the presser foot and continue.

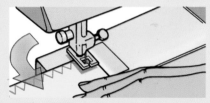

Fig. 3.62

Edge stitching

As the name implies the folded edge of each piece is stitched.

1 Turn a small hem to the wrong side around each piece before tacking into position.

2 Set a medium length machine stitch and carefully sew all around each piece.

Fusing

This process uses a special adhesive called **bondaweb**. Bondaweb is a fine, non-woven fabric, covered in adhesive with a special paper backing. It is applied using an iron.

1 Cut out the fabric shapes that you want to appliqué.

2 Cut out the same shapes in bondaweb.

3 Put the bondaweb with paper side upwards on to the back of the fabric shape.

4 Iron over the paper and leave it to cool.

5 Carefully peel the paper backing away from the bondaweb.

6 Place the shape on to the background fabric.

7 Cover with a damp cloth and then iron the shape on to the fabric.

8 Leave it to cool.

Quilting

It is thought that the earliest quilting was simply a way of making fabrics last longer by stitching two worn pieces of fabric together. **English (block)** quilting involves sandwiching a layer of wadding (usually polyester) between two layers of fabric. The surface can then be stitched to form a decorative pattern. The layers trap air making quilted fabrics feel warm. Fabrics can be bought ready quilted, but with a little practice this is a fairly easy technique to learn. Interesting effects can be created by quilting shapes which can then be appliquéd on to your product, or by quilting features such as cuffs and pockets on coats or jackets.

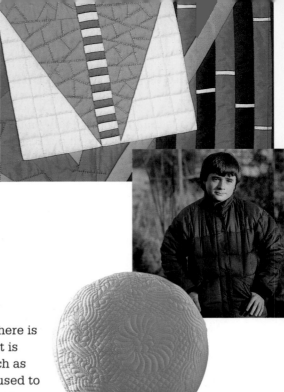

Choice of fabrics for quilting

Quilting is easier to work on fabrics which are not stretchy as there is always a possibility of the fabric stretching out of shape while it is being stitched. The background fabric can be a lining fabric such as acetate or a fine cotton. Fabric with a waterproof finish can be used to make articles such as bags for toiletries or baby items. Fig. 3.64 shows the steps involved in making quilted fabric.

Fig. 3.63
Quilting has many uses

Making a piece of quilted fabric

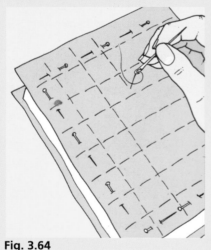

Fig. 3.64

1 Put the background fabric on to a flat surface. Place the wadding on top and then lay the top fabric over the wadding.

2 Pin the layers of fabric from the centre towards the edges, making sure that the layers remain smooth.

3 The layers of fabric need to be tacked together in a grid to prevent them slipping and puckering when stitching later. Start by tacking down the centre and then tack in parallel rows about 50 mm apart. Repeat this in the other direction to form the grid.

4 The fabric is now ready for stitching. This can be done by hand or machine. There should not be too many lines of stitching if the quilted fabric is to be used for insulation as this will prevent air being trapped.

Quilting by hand

1 Secure the thread on the wrong side of the fabric. Push the needle through the layers of fabric, making sure you keep it straight and not at an angle. This would cause the fabrics to pucker.

2 Push the needle back through the fabric again making a small stitch. Again make sure that the needle is kept straight.

3 Continue stitching in this way until the finished effect is created.

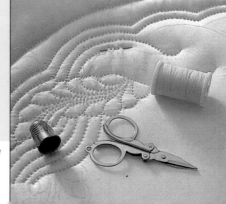

Fig. 3.65 *Quilting by hand*

Quilting by machine

This can be achieved using either a straight stitch or by using a narrow zig-zag to create an interesting effect. Traditional quilting uses lines of parallel stitching in different directions. It is important that these are kept even and straight to create a professional finish. However, interesting effects can be created by stitching in a more random way. Most machines are supplied with a special quilting foot as seen in Fig. 3.66. This has short turned up toes which allows the layers of fabric to pass through easily and a metal bar which can be adjusted to guide you in keeping the lines evenly spaced as you sew. You may also want to experiment using a twin needle or using a decorative embroidery stitch.

Fig. 3.66 *A quilting foot*

Machine quilting

1 Set a fairly long length machine stitch or long narrow zig-zag stitch.
2 Place the layers of fabric into the machine so that you can sew down the middle first.
3 Sew the first line of quilting ensuring that the layers of fabric are flat on the machine.
4 If you are using a quilting guide set this to the correct width and then place the fabric back into the machine so that the quilting guide runs along the first line of stitching.
5 Sew the next line,ensuring that the quilting guide runs along the previous stitching.
6 Continue sewing lines, using the quilting guide to help keep the stitching straight.
7 Remove all the tacking threads and secure the ends of sewing thread.

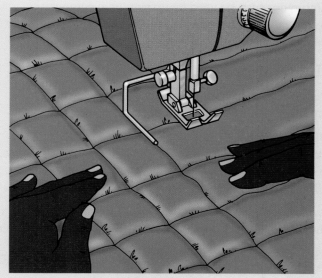

Fig. 3.67 *Machine quilting*

Fig. 3.68

Quilting can be used very effectively with other techniques. Try screen or block printing a design and then quilt around it. Fabric which has been silk painted or has a batik design can be quilted to add interest to particular areas of the design. Quilted designs can have further embroidery applied to them either by hand or machine or have beads sewn on to them. Fig. 3.68 shows some of the interesting effects that can be created using combinations of techniques.

Embroidery

Embroidery is a very traditional technique used for embellishing fabrics. A wide range of effects can be created according to the type of embroidery used, the threads and the colours chosen. Embroidery can be carried out by hand and while this is very time consuming very delicate designs can be created. Most sewing machines can be programmed to embroider a wide range of stitches. There are also an increasing number of machines which allow you to create your own embroidered motifs. Machines can be used for 'free' embroidery by lowering the feed, removing the presser foot and sewing in any direction on to the fabric which is stretched in a frame. Very subtle effects can be created by using threads which are the same colour as the fabric.

Embroidery can be used on its own or in combination with another technique such as appliqué, quilting or fabric printing to add detail to the design.

Fig. 3.69 *Embroidery machines*

Hand embroidery

Fig. 3.70 illustrates some of the more common embroidery stitches.

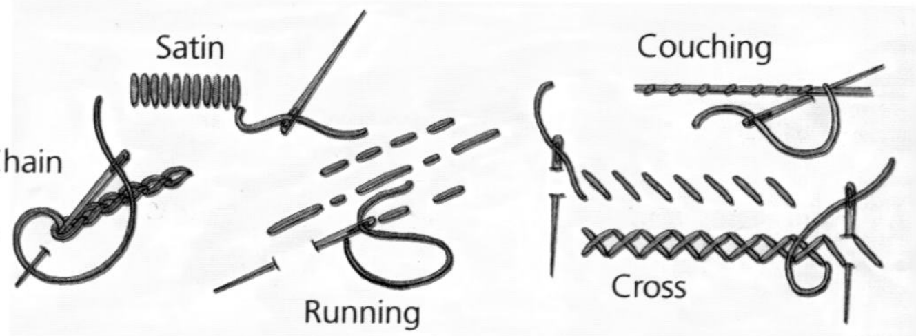

Different types of thread can be used including stranded embroidery thread, wool and metallic threads. A crewel needle is used as this has a long eye which allows the thread to pass through easily.

It is a good idea to place the fabric into an embroidery ring as this keeps the fabric flat and prevents the stitches from being pulled too tightly.

Satin Couching Chain Running Cross

Fig. 3.70

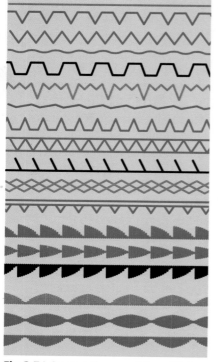

Fig 3.71 *Decorative machine stitches*

Machine embroidery

Pre-programmed decorative stitches are available on many sewing machines. These can be sewn in rows on products to add interest, or can be sewn on to another piece of fabric which can then be appliquéd on to the background.

Some machines can be used with a computer so that you can develop your own design and then sew this on the machine. These designs are best if they are kept fairly simple and bold. This equipment is useful for sewing badges and motifs which can then be appliquéd on to your product.

It is a good idea to apply some iron-on interfacing to the back of the fabric before embroidering.

This makes the fabric firmer and prevents the fabric from stretching while it is being stitched.

Fabric needs to be tightly stretched into an embroidery ring before sewing. Fig. 3.72 shows how to do this.

Fig. 3.72 *Fabric being placed in embroidery ring.*

'Free' machine embroidery

Interesting and diverse effects can be created when using this type of embroidery. There is always a danger that needles will break so the following tips need to be observed.

Fig. 3.74 *'Free' machine embroidery*

1   Iron lightweight interfacing to the back of the fabric before sewing.
2   Make sure the fabric is tightly stretched in an embroidery ring.
3   Lower the feed on the machine and remove the presser foot.
4   Put the ring in position under the needle and remember to lower the presser foot (even though the actual foot is not attached, as this will engage the tension correctly).
5   Bring the lower thread through to the top of the fabric. Turn the balance wheel towards you until the needle has come back out of the fabric and is at its highest point. Gently pull the top thread up and pull the lower thread through.
6   Hold both threads securely when starting to sew. Trim them off after a few stitches.
7   Move the frame smoothly as you work.

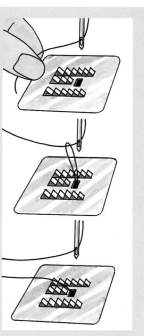

Fig. 3.73

Using braid, ribbon and lace

A wide range of plain and patterned braids and ribbons can be bought in a variety of widths. Manufacturers often use braid containing their name or logo on products (Fig. 3.75).

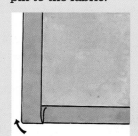

Fig. 3.75

These items can be applied to form patterns or in lines using hand or machine stitching. Straight machine stitching is usually used as the braid or ribbon is providing the decorative detail, but decorative stitching can also be used effectively on ribbon. Braid, ribbons and lace need to be tacked securely before sewing so that they do not slip out of place. Problems always occur on corners. The diagrams in Fig 3.76 show you how to deal with these.

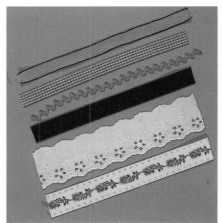

Fig. 3.77
Braid, ribbon and lace

How to turn corners

1   Pin first edge of braid in place.
2   Just before you reach an edge, fold the unpinned side of the braid across at right angles. This edge now becomes the section to pin to the fabric.
3   Make sure that the fold is level with the free edge of the fabric.
4   Tack, remove pins and sew in place.

Fig. 3.76

4 PRODUCTS & PRODUCT DESIGN

In industry products are designed and made to earn money and create wealth. Industrialised nations which do this successfully enjoy a high standard of living. Money created by industry helps to pay for hospitals, housing, and roads.

Fig. 4.1 *Machinery meant that fabric could be mass produced*

Manufacturing

Clothing is one of the basic human needs, along with shelter, food and warmth. Stone-age man used animal skins for clothing. Later, fabric for clothes and other household textiles was made in the home. Natural dyes from plants were used to colour fibres and fabrics. Young girls in the family would spin wool to be woven. This gave rise to the term 'spinster' to describe an unmarried woman. Weaving was often carried out in small sheds attached to houses.

As industry developed the manufacture of fabrics and textile items moved away from the home to industrialised regions, such as the north of England. Fabric was mass produced in mills, using machinery. The earliest weaving looms were large, noisy and dangerous. Looms used today are much safer and faster, with the ability to create large amounts of fabric in an hour. The manufacture of clothing and household textile items also moved from the home. Tailors or dressmakers in towns produced garments as one off jobs or in small scale batches. Eventually factories were set up where clothing could be mass produced. This gave ordinary people a chance to buy cheaper clothing, and allowed them a more varied range of clothes.

Fig. 4.2 *Modern textile manufacture*

These days almost all clothing is mass produced. However, clothing can be used as a fashion statement. It is the demand for changing fashions which causes the need for new designs each season.

Consumer pull

New products are often developed in response to demands of consumers. Products are often evaluated as part of consumer research. Frequently this leads to the design and development of new products. This is known as 'consumer pull'. As long as consumers make demands for new or improved products they will be designed to meet their requirements.

Technology push

Products are also designed to make use of new technology. Old products are redesigned or updated to enable technological developments to be used. The design and manufacture of new materials with unique properties leads to new products. For example, the development of Lycra allowed a whole range of brightly coloured dance and sports wear to be produced. This is known as 'technology push' - as new technology 'pushes' forward the design of a product.

Fig. 4.3 *Lycra is often used in sportswear*

Fig. 4.4 *Developments in fabric have caused swimming costume styles to change over time*

Developing a new product

Products are usually designed as a result of consumer pull or technology push. The following case study shows how one company designs and makes products to meet the consumer pull for new styles and colours in clothing.

Case study–Henri-Lloyd Ltd

You may not be familiar with the name Henri-Lloyd, but you will probably be aware of many of their products through their promotion of high profile sporting events. For example, the Whitbread Round the World Yacht Race (see Fig. 4.6).

Fig. 4.5 *The logo of Henri-Lloyd Ltd*

Background

Henri-Lloyd is a British clothing company with their headquarters in Worsley, in the outskirts of Manchester. The company was founded in 1963 by Henri Strzelecki in partnership with Angus Lloyd. Henri-Lloyd now have teams of designers in Britain and Italy who work together to produce the jackets, knitwear, jeans and T-shirts which make up the Henri Lloyd fashion ranges. The technical range, which includes garments for foul weather is designed by the in-house team.

Henri-Lloyd is involved in the development of high specification technical clothing for professional explorers and adventurers. They are licensed to use Gore-tex® in their garments. Gore-tex® is a synthetic membrane (film) with unique properties. It allows moisture from the body to be moved through the fabric to the outside, but does not allow moisture from outside to pass through the fabric. Gore-tex® is sometimes used alone and sometimes sealed to a breathable fabric also produced by W.L. Gore Ltd. This guarantees a waterproof layer which is an essential criterion in some clothing products and a desirable one in others.

Fig. 4.6

The design process

The design process used in school is a framework to help you learn how to design things. Professional designers do not always work in exactly the same way. They develop a process which suits them and the products they are working on. In the textiles industry it is often necessary to begin work by predicting what will be 'in fashion' in one or two years time.

The design brief

At Henri Lloyd designers are asked to provide new concepts (ideas) each year for clothes that will complement existing products. The styles of garments are divided in to the **fashion market** and the **sailing market** (which caters for dedicated sports people). Garments produced for the sailing market may be worn by adventurous explorers walking to the south pole, or round-the-world yacht crews. These products have to meet high specifications in terms of water resistance and warmth. In this case study we will follow the design and manufacture of a jacket for the fashion market.

The specification

Designers are not asked to draw up a detailed specification at this stage. Specifications for sizes and fabric weave already exist within the company. These will be used at the production planning stage later in the design process. The specification that designers have to work with will refer to the structure of the **range** for the season. This will tell them details such as:

- the number of jackets to be designed;
- the shapes of the jackets, for example fitted or baggy;
- the number of shirts or T-shirts to be included;
- the styles of trousers to be produced, for example 'boot leg', 'drain-pipe', or 'bags';
- fabrics will be carefully investigated and chosen at this early stage according to fashion predictions for the coming year.

Some ideas for the type of fabric to be used may also be included, according to the fashion predictions for the coming year.

Fig. 4.7 *Henri-Lloyd designs have to be hard-wearing and look good*

Predicting fashions

In the fashion market, Henri-Lloyd produce new styles for the two main seasons, winter and summer. Designers have to work on the concept for the fashion range at least one year in advance. In January each year designers have to present their completed ideas at a conference to launch the range to the UK and overseas sales teams. This is where the winter designs for the following year are shown. These items have to be made and delivered to the shops by the end of autumn for the winter selling period. In June, Henri-Lloyd's designers will launch the designs for the following summer.

The main difficulty in designing a fashion product is predicting the shapes and colours which will be in fashion in the future. One of the things designers use to help them keep up with changing fashions is a list of the films which are being planned for release in the future. When the film *Grease* was re-released short trousers ('peddle pushers') became very fashionable. Similarly, the film *Mulan* inspired a range of Chinese style clothing for children.

Market research

Within the fashion industry there are groups of people who spend their working lives predicting what colours and shapes will be fashionable in the coming years. Henri-Lloyd's designers refer to the industry colour forecast INDE to help them decide which colours should be included in a new range. INDE is a market research business which companies can subscribe to. The research company use a wide range of strategies to help them forecast what might be fashionable up to two years in the future. It is more economical for Henri-Lloyd to buy this information from the research company than to set up their own market research.

Developing ideas

When Henri-Lloyd's designers begin to develop new designs they need to make a wide range of decisions. For example:

- Which shape of jacket – fitted or blouson?
- Will the sleeves be inset or raglan?
- What style of cuff?
- How many pockets should be included?
- Should the collar be high standing, crewe or flat?

Fig. 4.8 *Jackets showing different combinations of sleeves, collars and pockets*

Decisions are made on all of these points and various combinations are drawn out for presentation.

The choice of fabric is very important, each season different fabrics are fashionable. Jackets could be made from gaberdine, woollen fabric, shower proof nylon or rip-stop nylon. A wide variety of finishes may be applied to the fabric. A glazed satinised finish is sometimes fashionable, but in other seasons a rubberised finish might be more up-to-date.

Fig. 4.9 *Fashionable fastenings*

Designers need to be aware of fashion trends in fastenings as well as in the colour and shape of garments. At different times all of the fastenings illustrated in Fig. 4.10 have been fashionable. When the style and materials needed for the jacket have been chosen, more drawings of the jacket will be made, with swatches of the fabrics attached to them. The fabrics will be shown in the different colours which are being suggested for use in the coming season. Buttons or other fastenings and items such as cord or toggles which are to be used will also be included. These are then presented to the product development team for final consideration and approval.

Prototype

When the product development team have made a final decision based on the drawings, a **prototype** will be produced. Prototypes or 'mock ups' are made up from the drawings to allow the jacket to be viewed in 3D form. To do this the design sketches are passed to the pattern technicians who produce a paper pattern on the computer. This is then used to make up the garment. At Henri Lloyd wherever possible the correct or similar fabric will be used in order to see how the fabric works in a particular style, e.g. will a fabric hang correctly? In some companies a prototype will be made from any fabric which is available, or is inexpensive. The intention is to see the final shape, fit and detail of the jacket.

Costing

The cost of each jacket is worked out in three parts. The cost of fabric, thread and fastenings is known as the variable cost. This cost varies (changes) constantly depending on the amount and type of materials used. The cost of running the factory, including wages, transport and packaging, is known as the semi-variable cost. This cost changes slowly each year. Finally a 'profit margin' is added. This must cover any other overheads (expenses) and leave a profit for Henri-Lloyd and the shops where the jackets are sold.

To work out the variable cost for each jacket, see the example for a single jacket below:

2 metres of fabric used at £5.00 per metre	= £10.00
Add the cost of zips, buttons, lining material and thread	= £3.50
This means the total variable cost	= £13.50

To work out the semi-variable cost for each jacket, the total semi-variable cost is divided by the amount of production time available.

For example, if the total semi-variable costs	= £10,000.00
And the total time of production (in minutes)	= £40,000.00
Then the cost per minute	= 0.25 (or 25 pence per minute)

If a jacket takes 45 minutes to make, the semi-variable cost is 25p X 45(minutes) = £11.25.

The total cost of manufacturing = £13.50 (the variable cost) + £11.25 (the semi-variable cost) = £28.75. A sensible profit margin is then added to this, before it is sold to the customer.

NB Please note that the figures shown are examples only and not actual costs of Henri-Lloyd Ltd.

Samples

When the final designs and costs have been approved the 'sample machinists' are asked to make up samples of each garment. Sample machinists are experienced workers who have a high standard of skill. These machinists must manufacture high-quality products which set the standard for the garments made by other workers. The samples produced at this stage are used by the sales force to sell the garments to shops. Using samples from the range the sales force visit the shops which stock this type of garment and take orders for the products. This is called **bulk sampling**.

Fig. 4.10 *Fashion and technical jackets*

Taking orders

Some companies manufacture a specified number of products then aim to sell these. 'Over-runs' may be sold in a factory shop at a reduced price. At Henri-Lloyd the orders are taken first and then the order books are 'closed'. This means that no further orders will be taken and only sufficient garments are made up to meet the orders. The jackets are made in time to be delivered to shops at the beginning of the season. This is an example of JIT ('Just In Time') production. By producing jackets in time for delivery to the shops the company do not have to spend large amounts of money on storage of completed garments over a long period. They are also able to order the components required for manufacture as they need them. This saves Henri-Lloyd having to order and pay for stock which they will not need immediately.

Target market

The fashion products produced by Henri-Lloyd are marketed to the youth market: young people around 16 to 25 years of age. These are the young people who have sufficient money to spend on fashion items and are prepared to pay a premium price for prestigious brand labels. The main competitors in this section of the market are Timberland® and Rockport®.

Fig. 4.11 *Timberland is one of Henri-Lloyds main competitors*

Marketing

Marketing involves making people want to buy the product you are producing. To market their jackets Henri-Lloyd sales and marketing staff need to consider four main issues. These are referred to as the 4 P's in the marketing mix.

- **Price** – The jackets being sold must be of a similar price to those of their competitors, if they are too expensive sales will be lost.
- **Place** – the type of shops which stock the jacket must be places which young people visit. Magazines carrying advertisements for garments must be aimed at young people in the 16–25 age range.
- **Product** – The jackets must be seen as fashionable, but they should also represent value for money – a high quality product which is fashionable and a status symbol.
- **Promotion** – The jackets are promoted through linking the brand name with prestigious sporting events, such as the Whitbread Round the World Yacht Race. Henri-Lloyd also supported Ranulph Fiennes in his Transglobe Expedition (See Fig. 4.12)

Fig. 4.12 *Ranulph Fiennes at the South Pole*

Manufacturing

All the jackets which have been ordered are made by batch production. Batch production allows a specific number of jackets to be made in one production run. The level of skill demanded of the workers is quite high.

Fig. 4.13 *Pattern pieces on screen*

Preparation

When samples have been finalised patterns are prepared for the whole size range. These are developed using block patterns stored in the computer. A block pattern is a basic pattern which brings together the correct measurements for each size in scale. For example, the sleeve length, chest, waist and leg. Pattern technicians select a suitable block and draw on style features, such as pockets and cuffs. All the pattern makings like notches are shown on the pattern.

Lay planning

Once the pattern has been finalised and all the details have been checked it is ready for a procedure called lay planning. The pattern layout is worked out using a computer program which minimises the wastage of fabric. This produces a garment pattern on one large sheet of paper which is placed on the fabric ready for cutting.

Fig. 4.14 *Cutting out*

Several layers of fabric are laid together. The number of layers will depend on the thickness of the fabric. The lay plan is placed on the fabric and it is cut using a Vacuum Gerber. This is similar to a band saw and is able to cut through several layers of fabric at once. The cutting blade is controlled by computer.

Logo

Every jacket has the Henri-Lloyd logo embroidered on it. This is done before the pieces are joined together by a bank of computerised embroidery machines. These machines are operated by computer and are able to embroider as many as 12 logos at once.

Fig. 4.15 *Embroidering logos*

Machining

Once the logo is in place the jackets are sewn together by skilled machinists. The pattern pieces are fastened together in bundles, and each bundle consists of one section of the jacket. Each machinist completes one task on every jacket. For example, one person will sew the sew the small pieces like the pockets and cuff tabs. Another will construct the garment stitching the sleeves, fronts and backs. The lining is then added and the collar attached. As each section is completed the bundle is passed to the next machinist in the process. Finally, the jacket is completed and ready for final inspection and packaging.

Fig. 4.16 *Machinists working on jackets*

Quality assurance

It is the responsibility of designers and manufacturers to ensure that their products deliver the highest standards the customer expects. Henri-Lloyd jackets are considered high quality products, and customers expect them to be fashionable, long-lasting and hard-wearing. To offer this assurance to customers many quality assurance systems are in place. These include a system of quality control checks which are used throughout the manufacturing process. The quality of design is as important as the quality of manufacture. Well designed jackets will be comfortable to wear, easy to fasten and the pocket will be of a suitable size to prevent items falling out.

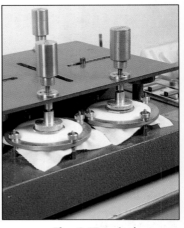

Fig. 4.17 *In industry an abrasion machine can be used to test how well a fabric will resist wear and tear*

Quality control

Throughout the production of the jackets the quality is carefully monitored. The fabrics which are selected for the jacket are sent to BTTG (British Textile Testing Group). Here the fabric undergoes rigorous tests. These tests include checking that the fabric is colour fast – the colour must not run in wet weather or during cleaning. The fabric is also tested for wear as the jackets have to continue to look good with no pilling or holes appearing in areas which take the most wear and tear.

Sealed samples

One of the machinists will make up a complete jacket. This sample is placed in a sealed bag and is used to check other jackets against. In some companies this may be known as the 'gold seal'.

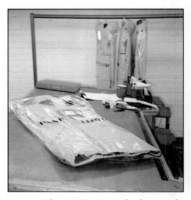

Fig. 4.18 *A sealed sample*

At different stages in the manufacturing process random samples are removed from the production line and tested. These tests include checking the length of the stitches, straightness and strength of seams, and correct seam allowance. All fastenings will be checked to ensure that they are well sewn on and that they work. Any work which does not pass the quality control will be returned to the machinist for correction. If this is not possible the product will be rejected.

Fig. 4.20 *Quality control testing*

At the end of the line random samples of completed jackets will be taken for further testing. As all of the jackets contain a layer of Gore-tex® in their construction they must be tested for their ability to withstand water. This is a condition of the license granted to Henri-Lloyd which allows them to use Gore-tex®. The jackets must be able to remain dry on the inside when they have been immersed in water.

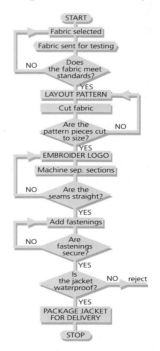

START
Fabric selected
Fabric sent for testing
NO ← Does the fabric meet standards?
YES
LAYOUT PATTERN
Cut fabric
Are the pattern pieces cut to size? → NO
YES
EMBROIDER LOGO
Machine sep. sections
NO ← Are the seams straight?
YES
Add fastenings
NO ← Are fastenings secure?
YES
Is the jacket waterproof? → NO → reject
YES
PACKAGE JACKET FOR DELIVERY
STOP

Fig. 4.19 *Quality control process*

Technical jackets

This term refers to technical jackets which will be used in emergency situations, such as life-jackets. It also includes sailing jackets and the high specification jackets worn by adventurers such as Sir Ranulph Feinnes who explore the Arctic regions, or Tracy Edwards who captained the first all female crew in the Whitbread Round the World Yacht Race. These people rely on their clothing for survival. If their jacket allowed water inside, their lives would be at risk. These technical jackets must all be tested individually.

Fig. 4.21 *Henri-Lloyd jackets can save lives – here Tracy Edwards wears an abandonment suit by Henri Lloyd*

Packaging

The jackets are all put on hangers and packaged in a protective layer of polythene for transport to the retailer. This packaging is removed once the jackets are put on display in the shops. Customers buying clothing like to be able to feel the fabric and, of course, try on the jackets. Any form of packaging would prevent this.

Fig. 4.22 *Packaged jackets*

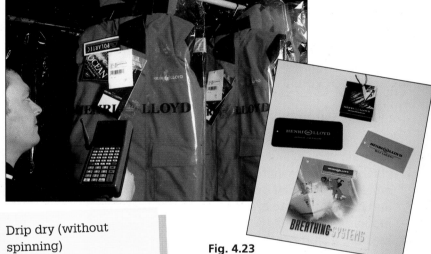

Fig. 4.23 *Swing labels*

Swing labels

Customer information is given on the swing labels attached to the jackets. Some of this information must be supplied by law.

Care labelling

Care labels are given on the swing labels attached to jackets and are also permanently sewn into the jackets. They must show the fibre content of the fabric and also give clear instructions for cleaning and care of the garment. The International Textile Care Labelling Code (ITCLC) is used and this is common to all countries in the European Union. These labels are shown opposite.

Fig. 4.24 *The ITCLC*

Washing

- ⊠ Do not wash
- Hand wash only
- 〔40〕 Wash at 40°C (temp shown) normal agitation, rinsing and spinning
- 〔40〕 Wash at temp shown but reduced agitation, gradual cooling and reduced spinning.
- 〔40〕 Wash at temp shown with very little agitation. Rinsing and spinning normal.

NB Different temperatures will be shown in the 'tubs'.

Drying

- Tumble Dry
- ⊠ Do not tumble dry
- ⫼ Drip dry (without spinning)
- ⊟ Dry flat
- ⊡ Hang to dry (after spinning)

Dry Cleaning

- Ⓟ Dry clean
- ⊗ Do not dry clean

(The symbol shows the dry cleaner which solvent to use)

Bleaching

- △ Chlorine bleach may be used
- ⊠ Do not bleach

Ironing

- ⊿ Cool iron
- ⊿ Warm iron
- ⊿ Hot iron
- ⊠ Do not iron

The future

Smart fabrics

Much of the recent research in textiles has focused on the development of new fibres. These have improved properties, are environmentally friendly and are relatively cheap to produce. One example of a new fibre is Tencela – microfibres and fibres developed from vegetable sources. However, scientists have become interested in a completely new area of research – the development of 'smart fabrics'. These are fabrics that have tiny microprocessors woven into them. 'Smart fabrics' will give wearers more freedom by reducing the need for heavy or expensive equipment. In the future, as well as wearing an item of clothing, you could be carrying a computer around with you!

Fig 4.25 *The red hat in this picture has a solar panel that powers a mobile phone. The grey coat can pick up e-mail messages and project them onto the wearers glasses*

Try to imagine:

- wearing a ball gown embroidered with LEDs (light emitting diodes) and switches;
- climbers wearing suits which would monitor their oxygen levels and prompt them to breathe more regularly;
- wearing a shirt capable of translating your speech into any language;
- deep sea divers wearing suits which maintain their oxygen and nitrogen levels, and keep them warm;
- underwear with sensors which react to maintain an even temperature wherever you are;
- surfing the internet and receiving or sending e-mail, whilst walking down the street.

Fig 4.26 *Pointing the ring at the label of a museum exhibit transmits information about it to the users headset*

Fig 4.27 *This jacket senses speech and plays an immediate translation to the wearer*

None of these developments are available yet. But, there are ways that you may be able to incorporate electronic circuits into your own designs. For example LEDs could be used in a glove puppet so that the eyes 'light up' when the fingers are pressed together. You could use an LDR (light dependent resistor) to activate flashing LEDs as part of a body belt, jacket or bag to be worn by cyclists at night. You could also make an interactive picture for small children – it could make sounds, or use LEDs to make it 'light up' when a child presses a part of the picture.

Things to do

1. Design a futuristic item of clothing or an accessory that you could wear to enable you to listen to your favourite music.
2. Surf the internet to see what you can find out about these developments. Start with IBM's research site at http://www.research.ibm.com. Put your ideas into an electronic presentation for your school's web site.

ACKNOWLEDGEMENTS

The publishers would like to thank the following for their help
in researching and providing material:

Daniel White at Henri-Lloyd Ltd

Lynda Lawson and Janet Russell, Young Textile Group (of The
Embroiderers' Guild)

Rob Jones, Specialist Crafts Ltd

Mark Cantrell

John P Robson

Martin and Roly Sookias

Anita Hallam, The Society of Dyers and Colourists

Allsport (4.8)
Chris Barton (2.11)
John Birdsall (1.80)
Brother (3.27, 3.29)
Bubbles (1.32)
BWMB (2.32)
Bruce Coleman Collection (2.32)
Collections (2.11, 2.32)
Sue Cunningham Photographic (2.36)
Dylon (2.49, 3.59)
Mary Evans Photo Library (4.2)
Gerber Ltd (3.4)
Getty Images (1.24, 2.15, 2.61)
Sally and Richard Greenhill (1.5)
Henri-Lloyd Ltd (4.7, 4.8, 4.10, 4.13, 4.15, 4.16, 4.17, 4.19, 4.20)
Holt Studios (2.36)
Jacqui Hurst (3.18, 3.59, 3.63, 3.74)
Andrew Lambert (4.18)
Marabu (2.55)
Angus Mill (2.20, 2.21, 3.10)
Hannah Paton (3.68)
Rex Features (1.68)
Science Photo Library (2.2, 2.22, 2.25, 2.34, 2.35, 2.37, 2.38, 3.40
The Silk Museum (2.16)
Martin Sookias (1.79, 2.19, 2.26, 2.29, 2.30, 2.31, 2.33, 2.47, 2.67, 2.69,
3.53, 3.56, 3.63, 3.75, 3.77)
Specialist Crafts Ltd (2.53, 2.56, 2.57, 2.71, 3.5)
Stihl (2.45)
Still Pictures (2.23, 2.24)
The Stock Market (2.32)
Techsoft (1.57, 2.64, 3.69)
Telegraph Colour Library (1.6, 1.7, 1.17, 1.52, 1.66, 2.1, 2.45, 4.3, 4.4)
Timberland (4.12)
Travel Ink (2.14)

Note to teachers

Collins Textiles Foundation Course has been written to suit National Curriculum Textiles Technology at Key Stage 3. Following the hugely successful Collins Design and Technology Foundation Course. It includes up-to-date material on skills and processes used in the textiles industry. An in-depth case study of real-life new products from concept to manufacture enhances pupils understanding of the designing and making process.

Throughout the book you will find questions related to the material on the page, and safety issues are highlighted wherever they are relevant.

Be aware of safety. Look for the symbol:

This book provides a solid foundation for GCSE Textiles Technology, as well as GNVQ Manufacturing.

Other titles in the series are: *Collins Design and Technology Foundation Course* and *Collins Food Foundation Course*.

INDEX